THE CAMBRIDGE SERIES OF PHYSICAL CHEMISTRY

GENERAL EDITOR
E. K. RIDEAL
Professor of Colloid Science in the
University of Cambridge

THE DIFFRACTION OF X-RAYS AND ELECTRONS BY FREE MOLECULES

THE
DIFFRACTION OF X-RAYS
AND
ELECTRONS BY FREE
MOLECULES

BY

M. H. PIRENNE
Dr.Sc. (Liège)

CAMBRIDGE
AT THE UNIVERSITY PRESS
1946

CAMBRIDGE
UNIVERSITY PRESS
LONDON: BENTLEY HOUSE
NEW YORK, TORONTO, BOMBAY
CALCUTTA, MADRAS: MACMILLAN

PRINTED IN GREAT BRITAIN AT THE UNIVERSITY PRESS, CAMBRIDGE

FOREWORD.

I LIKE Dr Pirenne's book on the X-ray and Electron diffraction of free molecules for several reasons.

It contains all essential information about a subject intimately connected with modern advances of our understanding of molecular structure in a mere 150 pages.

Consistently the theoretical development is logically followed through from its first beginning to the very end, without insisting on mathematical details, but always leading to the point where the actual magnitude of the effect is evaluated.

Nowhere is the experimental evidence neglected or the practical side treated superficially and at every occasion the theory is put to the test by confrontation.

P. DEBYE

CORNELL UNIVERSITY
ITHACA, N.Y.

April 1946

To

MY FATHER AND MOTHER

PREFACE

THE study of the diffraction of X-rays by gases is essentially the microscopy of isolated atoms and molecules. It gives information about the distribution of negative charges in these particles and consequently can determine the relative position of the atoms in a single molecule.

Although the general theoretical basis of the method was given in 1915 by Debye, positive experimental results were not obtained until 1928. The historical development of the method shows a harmonious interplay of theoretical and experimental investigations. The theory of the scattering of X-rays by free molecules is fundamentally a classical problem of light interference, but no satisfactory agreement with observation can be arrived at without making use of the quantum theory.

This monograph is intended primarily to give an account of the theoretical basis of the study of X-ray diffraction by gases and of the information it has yielded about the structure of atoms and molecules. But it would not be complete without taking into consideration the diffraction of fast electrons by gases, which is based on the same principle as the X-ray method. Again, the scattering of X-rays by atoms in crystals is discussed in relation to the scattering by free atoms, and the chapter on intermolecular interferences in gases is completed by a consideration of the diffraction of X-rays by liquids.

The chief aim is to give fundamental ideas and experimental results. Special attention has been paid to the hypotheses and principles underlying theories, as well as to their limits of validity. Mathematical formulae and numerical data of importance have been included, but extensive mathematical developments of the theories have generally been omitted, the reader being referred for them to the original publications.

It is therefore hoped that this work will be useful to all those who are interested in the properties of molecules and atoms, and that it will be of practical assistance to those doing experimental research in the field of molecular physics. A complete bibliography of the original literature has been attempted for X-ray diffraction by gases, but not for electron diffraction, which has already been extensively reviewed, or for fields such as X-ray diffraction by liquids, where significant references, however, have been chosen.

It gives me great pleasure to record here my thanks to Professor P. Debye for his interest in this work and his invaluable assistance, as well as for his hospitality at the Max Planck Institut at Berlin-Dahlem where, in 1938, the major part of this monograph was written. I am also much indebted to Dr L. Bewilogua of the same Institute for putting at my disposal his experience in the field of X-ray diffraction.

I am glad to express my gratitude to Professor L. D'Or and to the late Professor V. Henri, who initiated my work in this field when I was a student at the University of Liège. I am indebted to Dr K.J. Laidler and Dr D.P. Riley who corrected the English of the manuscript, and to Mr A. Maccoll who read the book in proof stage.

My thanks are offered to the Editors of the journals listed below for permission given to make use of figures and of a table. The exact reference will be found in each case printed with the figure: *Helvetica Physica Acta, Journal of Chemical Physics, Philosophical Magazine, Physical Review, Proceedings of the Cambridge Philosophical Society, Proceedings of the Royal Society, Reviews of Modern Physics.*

I am very grateful to Professor E.K. Rideal and to the Syndics and Staff of the Cambridge University Press for their never-failing help in the preparation of this book for publication under wartime conditions.

M. H. P.

THE ROYAL INSTITUTION
  LONDON
April 1946

CONTENTS

LIST OF IMPORTANT SYMBOLS

θ scattering angle, i.e. angle between incident ray and scattered ray. *The angle θ used in X-ray and electron diffraction by gases is equal to the X-ray crystallographer's 2θ.*

I_0 primary intensity.

I_s scattered intensity.

I_e X-ray intensity scattered by an electron according to classical theory. For unpolarized primary realization I_e is given by equation (3).

R distance to the scattering molecule.

λ wave-length. λ (e.g. in the universal variable $(\sin\frac{1}{2}\theta)/\lambda$) is expressed in A.

A.   Ångström unit; $1\,\text{A.} = 10^{-8}\,\text{cm}$.

ν frequency.

a_e $= 2\cdot81 \times 10^{-13}$ cm. is the classical radius of the electron, equation (2).

a_H $= 0\cdot53 \times 10^{-8}$ cm. is the 'radius' of the hydrogen atom, equation (13).

a Thomas-Fermi characteristic radius of the atom for coherent radiation, equation (18). a is also used to represent a length characterizing the dimension of an imaginary atom, equation (62).

b Heisenberg-Bewilogua characteristic radius of the atom for incoherent radiation, equation (27).

l_{ij} distance between the points, or atoms, i and j.

k $= 2\pi/\lambda$.

s $= 2\sin\frac{1}{2}\theta$ (s is also used to represent the 'screening constant' of an atom).

x_{ij} $= ksl_{ij} = 4\pi l_{ij}(\sin\frac{1}{2}\theta)/\lambda$.

Z atomic number.

f atomic scattering factor for X-rays, equation (9).

F atomic scattering factor for electrons, equation (47).

S incoherent scattering function according to Heisenberg-Bewilogua, equation (30).

Q relativity correction factor for incoherent radiation, equation (38).

V total volume.

Ω volume occupied by the particles contained in V.

W probability distribution function for a monatomic liquid.

$e^{-A_{ij}}$ correction factor for thermal vibrations in a molecule, equation (84).

D 'density function' of a molecule, equation (98) or (100).

h Planck's constant.

$-e$ charge of the electron.

m mass of the electron at rest.

c velocity of light.

μ linear absorption coefficient.

The table of 'Atomic scattering factors f' computed by James and Brindley [109] is reproduced at the end of this book (Table VIII, p. 145). Tables of 'X-ray emission spectra and absorption edges', and of 'Absorption coefficients' will be found in the second volume of the *International Tables for the Determination of Crystal Structures* [186]. They are also given in the books by Bragg [18] and by Compton and Allison [28]. A four-place table of $(\sin x)/x$ has been computed by Sherman [156] and is also reproduced in the book by Randall [149].

PLATE I

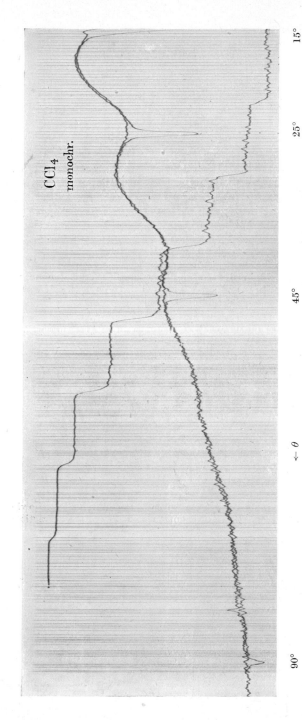

CCl₄
monochr.

← θ

90°   45°   25°   15°

Microphotometer record of a photographic diffraction pattern of crystal-reflected Mo Kα radiation by CCl₄ vapour. The stair-like trace gives the intensity calibration obtained using a rotating sector, the intensity of one step being to that of the next from right to left as 2 is to 3. The values given for the scattering angle θ are only approximate.

PLATE II

The apparatus of Fig. 78, fixed on to the X-ray tube. The crystal monochromator is between the X-ray tube and the primary slit. The cylindrical, water-cooled film holder is attached under the diffraction cell.

Detail view of the same apparatus, without the film holder, showing the entrance of the primary slit and the entrance window of the diffraction cell.

The same as above, dismounted.

CHAPTER 1

COHERENT SCATTERING

CLASSICAL THEORY OF SCATTERING BY ELECTRONS

In his book, published in 1903, on the *Conduction of Electricity through Gases*, Sir J.J. Thomson develops a theory of the radiation which is scattered when an X-ray beam passes through matter. A section entitled 'Theory of the secondary radiation' begins as follows: 'The secondary radiation is readily explained if we take the view, which we shall discuss later, that the Röntgen rays consist of exceedingly thin pulses of very intense electric and magnetic force. Let us suppose that such a pulse is travelling through a medium containing ions—it is not necessary that the ions should be free: when the pulse reaches a charged ion the ion will be acted on by a very intense force and its motion accelerated. Now when the velocity of a charged body is changing pulses of electric and magnetic force proceed from the body, the magnitude of these forces being proportional to the acceleration of the body: thus while the primary Röntgen pulse is passing over the ion and accelerating its motion, the ion gives out a pulse of electric and magnetic force— the secondary Röntgen pulse—the secondary pulse ceasing as soon as the acceleration of the ion vanishes, i.e. as soon as the primary pulse has passed over.'[†] The above statement constitutes the basis of the classical theory of X-ray scattering.

An isolated electron. Let us consider an electrically charged particle which is free, that is, which is so weakly bound that its proper period of motion is very great compared with the vibration period of the incident ray. Under the influence of electromagnetic radiation, such a particle oscillates at the same frequency as that of the radiation. It thus constitutes an oscillating dipole of the type studied by Hertz, and therefore emits secondary radiation of the same frequency as the primary radiation. The amplitude of the secondary radiation is inversely proportional to the mass of the

† See (163), 1st ed. p. 268.

particle. Accordingly, particles other than electrons play only a negligible role in X-ray diffraction. For instance, since the intensity is proportional to the square of the amplitude, the radiation scattered by a proton is $(1846)^2$ times weaker than that scattered by an electron.

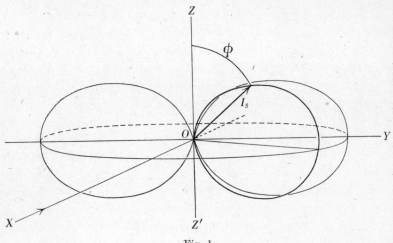

Fig. 1.

For primary radiation polarized in the plane XOZ and travelling in the direction XO (Fig. 1) it may be calculated[†] that the angular distribution of the intensity I_s scattered by an electron situated at O is given by

$$I_s = I_0 \frac{a_e^2}{R^2} \sin^2 \phi, \tag{1}$$

where I_0 is the primary intensity, ϕ the angle between the scattered ray and the direction OZ, R the distance from the observation point to O, and

$$a_e = \frac{e^2}{mc^2} = 2 \cdot 81 \times 10^{-13} \, \text{cm}. \tag{2}$$

is the classical radius of the electron, $-e$ being the charge of the electron, m the mass of the electron and c the velocity of light. Fig. 1 gives a vectorial representation of this intensity distribution. The intensity is zero in the directions OZ and OZ', because an oscillating dipole does not radiate energy along its axis.

† See (163), 3rd ed., vol. **2**, p. 256.

For completely unpolarized primary radiation travelling along $X'O$ (Fig. 2), the distribution of the scattered intensity I_e is given by

$$I_e = I_0 \frac{a_e^2}{R^2} \frac{1 + \cos^2 \theta}{2}, \qquad (3)$$

where θ, the scattering angle, is the angle between the scattered ray and OX, the direction of the primary ray.[†] The intensity distribution here is symmetrical around the direction of the incident radiation. Normal to the primary direction ($\theta = \frac{1}{2}\pi$), the scattered radiation is completely polarized and its intensity is reduced to one-half of its value in the OX direction ($\theta = 0$). The numerical factor $\frac{1}{2}(1 + \cos^2 \theta)$ is called the *polarization factor*.

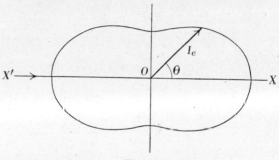

Fig. 2.

A rigid system of free electrons. The radiation scattered by an electron has the same frequency as the primary radiation and the phase difference between the two is therefore constant. Scattering of such a kind is said to be *coherent*. When several electrons scatter X-rays simultaneously, interferences must therefore be expected between the secondary rays originating from the different electrons. The intensity scattered in any direction is not simply the sum of the intensities scattered individually by each electron, and the intensity distribution is not given by formulae of types (1) or (3), as was at first supposed. For example, in the direction of the primary ray ($\theta = 0$), there is no phase difference between the rays scattered by the different electrons, and all the amplitudes are additive, so that the intensity becomes proportional to the square

[†] The scattering angle θ used in X-ray and electron diffraction by gases is equal to the X-ray crystallographer's 2θ.

of the number of electrons, n^2, and not simply to n. In fact, the existence of 'excess scattering' in the forward direction was early recognized (Fig. 3).

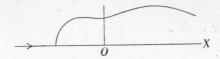

Fig. 3. Angular distribution of the scattering of X-rays by filter paper.
(After Owen (135).)

In 1915 Debye (32) investigated theoretically the scattering of X-rays by a rigid system of electrons (or of any diffracting points) which takes successively all possible orientations in space. It is clear that if a rigid system of electrons is placed in a given position in an X-ray beam, it must produce an interference pattern which can be received on a screen, in the same way as a system of small apertures gives with visible light the interference patterns of Young. If the system of electrons is a gas molecule, however, such interference patterns have so short a duration that they cannot be observed. It is possible to observe only the resultant intensity scattered over a period of time, during which the molecule has taken innumerable different positions relative to the primary beam. The problem therefore is to calculate the *mean intensity* scattered by the system of electrons for all possible spatial orientations, the structure of the system remaining invariable. This calculation must show whether the instantaneous interferences vanish from the observable average pattern, or not. In the calculation the system of electrons is taken to be rigid, that is, the mutual distances of the electrons remain constant. The electrons, nevertheless, are considered to be free as far as X-ray scattering is concerned. First, the intensity scattered by the system at an arbitrary orientation relative to the incident radiation is calculated. Secondly, the mean intensity is calculated, all orientations being considered equally probable. Debye's fundamental result is that the interference effects do not entirely cancel out in the mean intensity. On the contrary, they effect strongly the angular distribution of the mean scattered intensity, which is given by the calculation as a function of the distances between the various electrons which make up the rigid system.[†] *Notwithstanding the complete absence of any preferred orientation of the system of electrons, therefore, the observable diffraction pattern shows strong interference effects, and the distribution of intensity in this pattern is determined by the structure of the rigid system of electrons.*

As a concrete example, Fig. 4 represents a system of two electrons A and B kept at a constant distance l apart and diffracting a beam of X-rays travelling in the direction of the arrows; p is a photographic film receiving the secondary radiation. For any arbitrary orientation of AB the difference of phase at P_1 and P_2

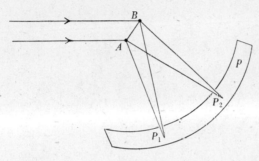

Fig. 4.

between the secondary rays issuing forth from A and B is in general not the same. Thus the resulting amplitudes, and intensities, are different at different points of the photographic film p. Dark and bright interference fringes appear on the latter. Now the system AB is placed successively in all possible orientations relative to the primary beam. For each orientation a new system of fringes is produced. The images of all these interference patterns become superimposed on the film. What is shown by the above calculation is that the resulting darkening of the film, far from being uniform, will present maxima and minima of intensity.

This is the basis of the method of diffraction of X-rays (or electrons) by gases.[‡] For a system constituted of the electrons $1, 2, ...,$

[†] For the special case of a diatomic molecule, a paper along the same lines was published simultaneously by Ehrenfest (66).
[‡] A simple treatment of the problem will be found in Debye (48).

$i, ..., j, ..., n$, and for unpolarized radiation of wave-length λ, the mean scattered intensity I_s is, according to Debye (32),

$$\bar{I}_s = I_0 \frac{a_e^2}{R^2} \frac{1 + \cos^2 \theta}{2} \sum_i \sum_j \frac{\sin \left(4\pi l_{ij} \dfrac{\sin \frac{1}{2}\theta}{\lambda} \right)}{4\pi l_{ij} \dfrac{\sin \frac{1}{2}\theta}{\lambda}}, \qquad (4)$$

where l_{ij} is the distance between electrons i and j, and the other symbols have their usual meaning. Using equation (3) and putting

$$x_{ij} = 4\pi l_{ij} \frac{\sin \frac{1}{2}\theta}{\lambda}, \qquad (5)$$

equation (4) can be written

$$\bar{I}_s = I_e \sum_i \sum_j \frac{\sin x_{ij}}{x_{ij}}. \qquad (6)$$

If I_e is taken as the unit of intensity, that is, if the intensity is always compared with that which a Thomson electron would scatter under the same conditions, $\bar{I}_s/I_e$ becomes a function of $(\sin \frac{1}{2}\theta)/\lambda$ only, and not of θ and λ separately. For a given system of electrons, intensity distributions $\bar{I}_s/I_e$ corresponding to different wave-lengths λ are therefore all represented by one and the same curve when they are plotted against the universal variable $(\sin \frac{1}{2}\theta)/\lambda$. This method of representation, which is very convenient because it allows one not to take the polarization factor $\frac{1}{2}(1 + \cos^2 \theta)$ explicitly into account, will be extensively used.

As an example, equation (6) may be developed for the case of a system of two electrons which remain at a constant distance l apart from each other. Since there are two electrons, 1 and 2, the term $\sum\sum$ is written

$$\frac{\sin x_{11}}{x_{11}} + \frac{\sin x_{12}}{x_{12}} + \frac{\sin x_{21}}{x_{21}} + \frac{\sin x_{22}}{x_{22}}.$$

It is obvious that $l_{12} = l_{21} = l$, and $l_{11} = l_{22} = 0$. Taking $(\sin x)/x = 1$ for $x = 0$, then

$$\frac{\bar{I}_s}{I_e} = 2\left(1 + \frac{\sin x}{x} \right), \qquad (7)$$

where $x = 4\pi l (\sin \frac{1}{2}\theta)/\lambda$.

To make the point clear, the elementary derivation of formula (7) is given here. The primary radiation is travelling along $Y'A$ (Fig. 5). The two electrons are A and B. The observation point P is in the plane XY. The other data are shown in the figure. First, the intensity of the scattered radiation at P will be calculated with the system AB immobile. The problem is to determine the phase difference, at P, of the rays emitted by A and B, and this is equivalent to determining the difference of optical path δ:

$$\delta = HB + BP - AP.$$

The wave-length λ is of the order of l, which is itself very small compared to R; under these conditions a brief calculation gives

$$\delta = 2l \sin \tfrac{1}{2}\theta \sin \alpha \cos (\phi + \tfrac{1}{2}\theta).$$

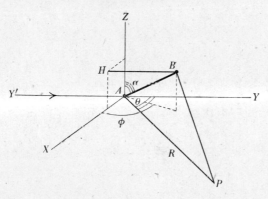

Fig. 5.

The amplitude of the resulting vibration at P is proportional to $\cos (\pi \delta / \lambda)$, and according to the above argument, the resulting intensity I_s is

$$I_s = 4I_e \cos^2 \left(\frac{\pi \delta}{\lambda}\right). \qquad (7a)$$

This intensity function is the analytical description of the instantaneous diffraction pattern mentioned above in connexion with Fig. 4. It is a function not only of the scattering angle θ, but also of the angles α and ϕ, that is, of the orientation of AB relative to the primary beam. The same is, of course, true of the corresponding amplitude.

The mean of I_s must now be taken giving an equal probability to all orientations of the system AB. The surface element of the sphere is $\sin\alpha\,d\alpha\,d\phi$; hence the mean value of $\cos^2(\pi\delta/\lambda)$ is given by

$$\frac{1}{4\pi}\iint \cos^2\left(2\pi\frac{l}{\lambda}\sin\tfrac{1}{2}\theta\,\sin\alpha\,\cos(\phi+\tfrac{1}{2}\theta)\right)\sin\alpha\,d\alpha\,d\phi.$$

The integration is performed by making a change of variable, $\phi+\tfrac{1}{2}\theta=\psi$, when the mean scattered intensity is found to be

$$\frac{\bar{I}_s}{I_e}=2\left[1+\frac{\sin\left(4\pi l\dfrac{\sin\tfrac{1}{2}\theta}{\lambda}\right)}{4\pi l\dfrac{\sin\tfrac{1}{2}\theta}{\lambda}}\right],\tag{8}$$

which is identical with (7).

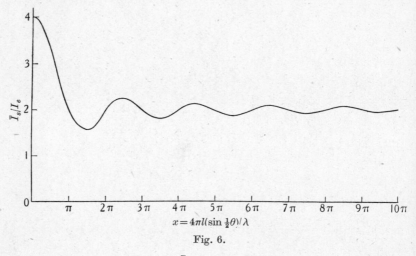

$$x=4\pi l(\sin\tfrac{1}{2}\theta)/\lambda$$

Fig. 6.

Fig. 6 represents the ratio $\bar{I}_s/I_e$ of equation (8) or (7), as a function of x. For very small values of $(\sin\tfrac{1}{2}\theta)/\lambda$, that is, for long wavelengths λ and small scattering angles θ, $\bar{I}_s$ tends to $4I_e$; the intensity is proportional to the square of the number of electrons which here is 2. On the other hand, for large values of $(\sin\tfrac{1}{2}\theta)/\lambda$, that is, for short λ and large θ, $\bar{I}_s$ tends to $2I_e$, which is the sum of the intensities of the radiation diffracted by two separate Thomson electrons. In order to study atoms and molecules, the dimensions of which are of the order of one Ångström unit (1 A. $= 10^{-8}$ cm.), the conditions must be chosen so as to get as many interference maxima as possible.

The values of θ are limited to 180°, but the wave-length λ can be varied: it must be of the order of 1 A. Fig. 7, which represents $\bar{I}_s/I_e$ in polar coordinates for the particular case where $\lambda = l$, shows that the angular distribution under these conditions is already very different from that of a single Thomson electron.

For a system of n electrons, n^2 terms ij appear in the double sum $\sum_i \sum_j$ of equation (6), among which n terms only are equal to unity, because for them $i = j$. When the number n of electrons increases, therefore, the relative importance of the periodic terms in equation (6) increases also. For n larger than 2, the curve no longer has necessarily the regularity of Fig. 6, as it is the result of the superposition of a number of $(\sin x)/x$ terms having in general different periods.

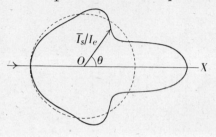

Fig. 7.

The systems of electrons studied above are imaginary. The principle of the theory nevertheless holds for actual molecules, as will be seen later, the atoms forming the molecule being taken as the diffracting centres.

The diffraction of X-rays by the electrons of actual atoms will now be considered. Although in fact the classical theory does not represent accurately the scattering of X-rays, the classically derived intensity I_e will be retained as a convenient unit.

COHERENT SCATTERING BY ATOMS

Definition of the atomic scattering factor. *The atomic scattering factor f of an atom is the ratio of the* **amplitude A_s** *of the radiation scattered by the atom to the amplitude A_e of the radiation which an electron would scatter under the same conditions according to the classical theory.* It is a numerical factor which gives, in Thomson units, the efficiency of the atom as a scatterer[†] of X-rays:

$$A_s = A_e f. \tag{9}$$

† Coherent scattering alone is considered here.

The intensity scattered by an isolated atom under given conditions is therefore (for unpolarized primary radiation)

$$I_s = I_e f^2. \tag{10}$$

Unless the atom possesses spherical symmetry, the amplitude A_s and the factor f depend, not only upon θ and λ, but also upon the orientation of the atom relative to the primary radiation. Such, for instance, would be the case for an atom containing the system of two electrons studied in the previous paragraph. If such an atom were a gas atom, one would observe only the *mean* value of the intensity I_s of equation $(7a)$ or (10), and this mean intensity, as has just been seen, is given, according to Debye, for formula (8). It may be pointed out that, knowing only this mean observable intensity $\bar{I}_s$, it is clearly impossible to derive from it the value of the scattering factor f. Such an operation is possible only when the atom is spherically symmetrical; then $\bar{I}_s = I_s$ and f can be derived from equation (10).

Now Bohr[13] in 1913 proposed for the helium atom a model similar to the above system of two electrons, and this model can therefore be tested by comparison with the results of X-ray diffraction by helium gas. The two electrons of the helium atom according to Bohr would move in the same orbit, always remaining at the opposite ends of a diameter of $0·63 \times 10^{-8}$ cm., with a frequency of the order of that of visible light. Fig. 8 compares the angular distribution of intensity calculated by formula (8) for $l = 0·63 \times 10^{-8}$ cm., with the distribution measured experimentally. The disagreement is striking, and the model suggested for the helium atom therefore cannot be accepted.

This discrepancy is not peculiar to the helium model. No model which represents an atom as a planetary system of point electrons moving in orbits around the nucleus has been brought into agreement with experimental data. On the other hand, the new quantum theory, which has radically changed ideas on atomic structure, is in excellent agreement with the measurements, as is shown for the case of helium in Fig. 8. According to the new theory the electronic atmosphere of the atom is diffuse, the electrons being distributed in a continuous 'charge cloud'. This conception arises from Schrödinger's theory, which implies Heisenberg's uncertainty principle, according to which there is no possibility of determining exactly both the position and the velocity of an electron. At any point there is an 'electron probability density' ρ, which, according to Schrödinger, is equal to the square ψ^2 of the wave-function ψ. Each volume element dV of the electron atmosphere is considered to scatter X-rays in the same way as a particle of charge $-\rho e\, dV = -\psi^2 e\, dV$ ($-e$ electron charge) would scatter according to the classical theory.

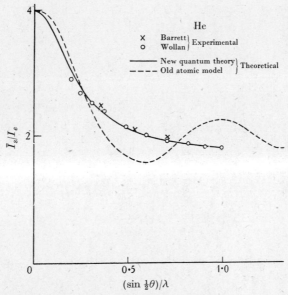

Fig. 8. Experimental and theoretical X-ray scattering functions for helium.
(After Wollan (178).)

The broken line which has been added in the present figure represents the scattering function calculated for the old helium model of Bohr.

According to wave-mechanics, the electron distribution of some atoms, as for instance the helium atom, is spherically symmetrical, and the electron distribution of many other atoms can be considered to be so without great error. In such cases, the question of the orientation of the atom relative to the primary radiation, of course, does not arise; the mean intensity scattered by a gas atom is given directly by equation (10), where f depends upon θ and λ only.

When the electron density probability ρ is a function $\rho(r)$ of the distance r to the atom centre only, the atomic scattering factor f, according to the classical theory (44), is given by

$$f = \int_0^\infty \rho(r)\, 4\pi r^2 \frac{\sin ksr}{ksr}\, dr, \tag{11}$$

where $k = 2\pi/\lambda$ and $s = 2\sin\frac{1}{2}\theta$. This equation is therefore the analytical expression of the amplitude A_s which results from the combination of the amplitudes scattered by all the various volume elements of the charge cloud of the atom, the amplitude A_e scattered by a Thomson electron being taken as unity. Thus, in the case of a spherically symmetrical electron atmosphere, the atomic scattering factor $f = A_s/A_e$ is a function of ks, or of the universal variable $(\sin\frac{1}{2}\theta)/\lambda$. When $(\sin\frac{1}{2}\theta)/\lambda$ is small, f tends to the value $\int_0^\infty \rho\, 4\pi r^2 dr$, which is equal to the total number of electrons in the atom.

The calculation of atomic scattering factors depends upon the knowledge of the function ρ. The simple case of the hydrogen atom will be considered first.

Hydrogen atom. Schrödinger's equation can be solved for the hydrogen atom. The wave-function for the normal state is

$$\psi = \frac{e^{-r/a_H}}{\sqrt{(\pi a_H^3)}}, \tag{12}$$

where

$$a_H = \frac{h^2}{4\pi^2 m e^2} = 0 \cdot 53 \times 10^{-8}\,\text{cm.} \tag{13}$$

is the 'radius' of the hydrogen atom and h is Planck's constant.[†] The electron density probability ρ is therefore

$$\rho = \psi^2 = \frac{e^{-2r/a_H}}{\pi a_H^3}, \tag{14}$$

and the atomic scattering factor f_H can be calculated using the general formula (11), the result being

$$f_H = \frac{1}{(1 + \frac{1}{4}(k^2 s^2 a_H^2))^2}. \tag{15}$$

Fig. 9 represents, as functions of r, the wave-function ψ, the

† See e.g. (77).

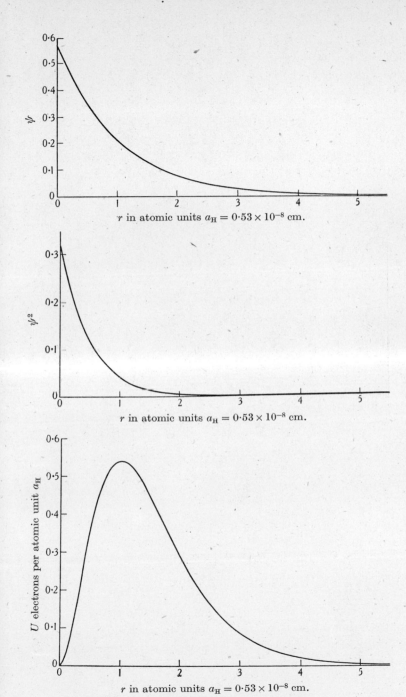

Fig. 9. The functions ψ, ψ^2 and $U = 4\pi r^2 \psi^2$ for the hydrogen atom in the normal state.

electron density probability $\rho = \psi^2$, and the electron radial distribution U, defined by the equation

$$U(r) = 4\pi r^2 \rho(r). \tag{16}$$

The density ρ is greatest near the nucleus and falls away as the distance r increases. The quantity $U(r)\,dr$ is the 'number' of electrons contained between two spherical shells of radii r and $r+dr$ having their centres at the nucleus; the function U has a maximum for $r = a_{\mathrm{H}}$.

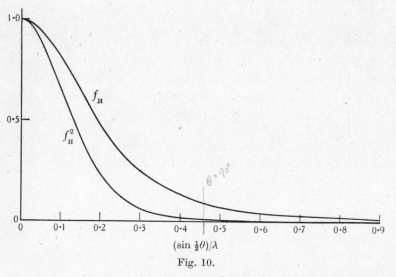

Fig. 10.

Fig. 10 represents the atomic scattering factor f_{H}, and its square f_{H}^2, plotted against $(\sin \tfrac{1}{2}\theta)/\lambda$. In the direction of the primary radiation an isolated hydrogen atom scatters like a Thomson electron, but as θ increases, the intensity decreases rapidly, unless the wave-length λ is very large. This is due to interferences arising in the electron atmosphere of the atom itself. For the $K\alpha$ radiation of copper ($\lambda = 1\cdot54$ A.), and for $\theta = 90°$, which corresponds to $(\sin \tfrac{1}{2}\theta)/\lambda = 0\cdot46$, $f_{\mathrm{H}}^2 = 0\cdot01$, which means that the intensity is a hundred times less than that which an electron would scatter classically. For very short wave-lengths, the H atom scatters practically no coherent radiation, except in directions very close to that of the primary radiation.

Other atoms. For many-electron atoms, Schrödinger's equation is too complicated to be solved exactly, and one must therefore resort to approximations of the electron distribution. The simplest of these approximations has been given independently by Thomas [161] and by Fermi [75].

The method of Thomas and Fermi. According to Thomas and Fermi [161,75], the Z electrons of an atom are considered as constituting a gas which is kept in equilibrium around the nucleus as a result of (*a*) the attraction between nucleus and electrons, (*b*) the repulsion between electrons and electrons, and (*c*) the kinetic energy of the electrons. The density of this gas is extremely great and consequently the zero-point energy of the electrons is considerable, so much so that their thermal energy is generally negligible in comparison. At ordinary temperatures this gas is therefore considered to be in a state of complete degeneracy: the kinetic energy of the electrons is taken as equal to their zero-point energy, and instead of using Boltzmann statistics as for ordinary gases, Fermi statistics [74] are used. These statistics are founded upon Pauli's exclusion principle, according to which two equivalent elements in a system cannot have all their quantum numbers correspondingly the same. It follows that at the absolute zero, instead of lying all on the lowest energy level, the Z electrons are distributed on the Z lowest levels, taking into account the existence of the spin. The result of this treatment is a spherically symmetrical electronic atmosphere,[†] the electron density ρ being

$$\rho = \frac{Z}{4\pi a^3} \left(\frac{\phi(x)}{x} \right)^{\frac{3}{2}}, \qquad (17)$$

where

$$a = \frac{1}{Z^{\frac{1}{3}}} \left(\frac{3}{32\pi^2} \right)^{\frac{2}{3}} \frac{h^2}{2me^2} = \frac{0\cdot47}{Z^{\frac{1}{3}}} \times 10^{-8}\,\text{cm.}; \qquad (18)$$

a is the characteristic radius of the atom of atomic number Z; $x = r/a$, r being the distance to the atom centre; $\phi(x)/x$ is the electrical potential in the system, measured in $Z\,e/a$ units.

The function ϕ has been numerically calculated by Fermi [75];

---

† It may be remarked [44] that this method corresponds exactly to that used by Debye for the study of the ion clouds in solutions of electrolytes, the only difference being that for solutions the ordinary Boltzmann statistics are used, while for electrons total degeneracy occurs and Fermi statistics are used.

ρ is therefore known and, using formula (11), the atomic scattering factor has been obtained (44). A numerical table of

$$\Phi = \frac{f}{Z}, \tag{19}$$

as a function of the variable

$$u = ksa = 4\pi a \frac{\sin \frac{1}{2}\theta}{\lambda} \tag{20}$$

has been computed (10) and is reproduced here (Table I). For any atom, the characteristic radius a must be determined according to equation (18), and the universal function Φ multiplied by Z then gives the value of the atomic scattering factor f as a function of $(\sin \frac{1}{2}\theta)/\lambda$. Fig. 11 represents the functions Φ and Φ^2. The intensity scattered by an isolated atom is $(Z\Phi)^2 I_e$. It is seen that $f = Z$ for $\theta = 0$. As θ increases, the intensity decreases, the more rapidly if λ is small and if a is large, that is, if Z is small. The larger the electron atmosphere compared to the wave-length, the more important are the destructive interferences occurring inside the atom.

TABLE I. *Coherent scattering function according to Thomas-Fermi.*
(After Bewilogua (10))

$u = ksa$	$\Phi = f/Z$	$u = ksa$	$\Phi = f/Z$	$u = ksa$	$\Phi = f/Z$
0·00	1·000	1·09	0·422	2·17	0·224
0·16	0·922	1·24	0·378	2·33	0·205
0·31	0·796	1·40	0·342	2·48	0·189
0·47	0·684	1·55	0·309	2·64	0·175
0·62	0·589	1·71	0·284	2·80	0·167
0·78	0·522	1·86	0·264	2·95	0·156
0·93	0·469	2·02	0·240	3·11	0·147

It is obvious that the Thomas-Fermi method does not reproduce exactly the details of the electron distribution in atoms, since no account is taken of the different $K, L, M, \ldots$ electron shells. It gives, nevertheless, a good approximation for heavy atoms in which the individual peculiarities of the shells are to some extent averaged out in the dense electronic atmosphere. Its advantage lies in the fact that it gives a general treatment applicable to all atoms. In order to attain a higher accuracy, the case of each particular atom must be treated individually. The Thomas-Fermi method is only applicable to neutral atoms.[†]

The method of Hartree. As an approximation to the solution of the Schrödinger equation for atoms containing several electrons,

[†] For a relativistic treatment of the Thomas-Fermi atom, see (166).

Hartree [91] has introduced the method of the 'self-consistent field', so called because it consists in finding a field of force which can be reproduced from the total distribution of charge given by the characteristic function of each electron in the field. The method is one of successive approximations. The distribution of charge in the

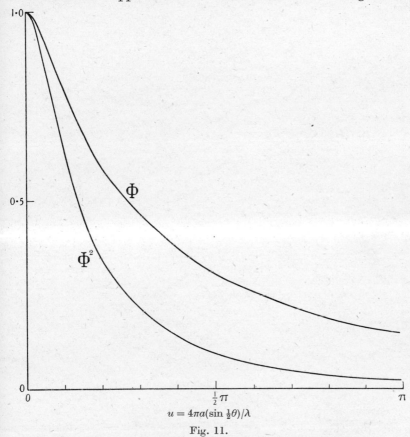

$$u = 4\pi a(\sin \tfrac{1}{2}\theta)/\lambda$$

Fig. 11.

self-consistent field is probably the best approximation to the actual distribution of charge in the atom which can be obtained without very much more elaborate theoretical and numerical work. An improvement of the method was made by Fock [76], who showed how the exchange phenomena between the equivalent electrons can be taken into account.† Dirac [62] has shown by what approximations

† This correction does not appear to have a great importance for the computation of the atomic scattering factors; see e.g. [92].

one can pass from the Hartree to the Thomas-Fermi model, and has given the theoretical justification of the latter model, showing what correction must be made in it to allow for exchange phenomena. Hartree's method allows the computation of the electron distribution in ions as well as in neutral atoms.

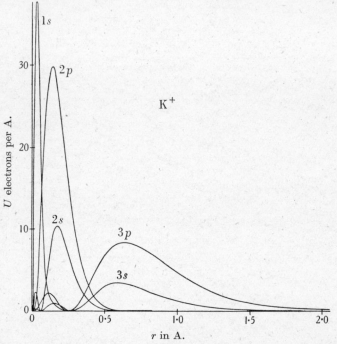

Fig. 12. Radial distribution of the different electron groups in the K⁺ ion.
(After James (111).)

Fig. 12 represents the radial distribution U, equation (16), of the various electron shells of the K⁺ ion, calculated by Hartree's method. Fig. 13 represents the contribution per electron of these different shells to the atomic scattering factor. The contribution of the electrons of the compact K shell remains important at high values of $(\sin \frac{1}{2}\theta)/\lambda$ and differs little from that of Thomson electrons, but it is far from being so for the other shells. For the M shell, which is much less dense and of much larger dimensions, the curves fall off rapidly and the ordinates can even become negative. The inner electrons therefore play a predominant role in the scattering of X-rays, the scattering being almost exclusively due to the K electrons for large values of $(\sin \frac{1}{2}\theta)/\lambda$. This is fortunate, in view of the fact that the distribution of the inner electrons is more accurately known than that of the outer, so that the uncertainty about the latter does not much matter.

The computation of the self-consistent fields requires a considerable amount of work. A table (reproduced on page 145) of scattering factors according to Hartree has been constructed by James and Brindley (109), using an interpolation method for atoms whose self-

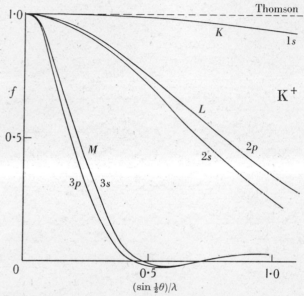

Fig. 13. Contribution to f of one electron in each of the electron groups of K^+.
(After James and Brindley (109).)

consistent fields had not been calculated. For Z greater than 20, however, the interpolation method cannot in general be used and one must resort to the Thomas-Fermi method. This is not a great inconvenience, because, as shown by Fig. 14 for the case of rubidium ($Z = 37$), the radial distribution curve according to Thomas-Fermi is a good average of Hartree's curve, which it intersects several times. Fig. 15 compares the f values for rubidium calculated by the two methods. It is seen that there is close agreement, the differences being partly due to the fact that the Thomas-Fermi curve applies to the neutral atom, while the Hartree curve is calculated for the ion.

There are other methods of obtaining atomic scattering factors.

Pauling and Sherman (136), for example, calculate them using hydrogen-like wave-functions with screening constants which are characteristic of each atom, but this method does not appear to be as reliable as that of Hartree.

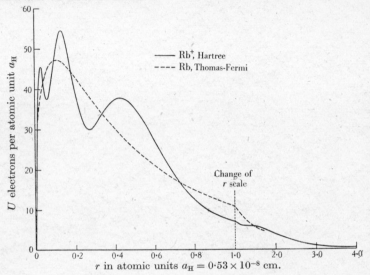

Fig. 14. Radial distribution of charge for rubidium, calculated first by Hartree's method of self-consistent field, and secondly by the method of Thomas and Fermi. (After Hartree (91).)

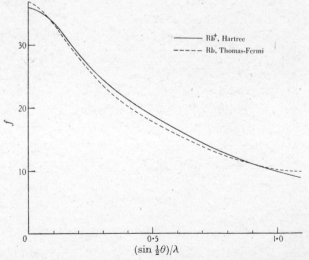

Fig. 15. Atomic scattering factor for rubidium, calculated first according to Hartree, and secondly according to Thomas and Fermi. (According to the data of James and Brindley (109).)

CHAPTER II

INCOHERENT SCATTERING

GENERAL

THE calculation of atomic scattering factors, as developed in the previous chapter, is done in two steps. First, the density of charge in the atom is calculated. Secondly, the radiation scattered by the charge cloud is determined. While the first step makes use of wave-mechanics explicitly, the second assumes that the electric charges in each volume element scatter according to classical theory. *A priori*, this assumption appears arbitrary, for the problem of scattering must be treated as a whole, and not in part only, according to the new quantum theory. The question, however, has been investigated in this way by Wentzel [173, 174] and Waller [170, 171, 172] who come to the conclusion that the above treatment leads to the correct result for the *coherent* intensity, and is therefore justified. Besides this coherent scattering, however, the theory also predicts the existence of *incoherent* scattering, which is due to the Compton effect.[†] In the new quantum theory, coherent and incoherent scattering constitute only one problem, and must be treated simultaneously.

While the frequency of the coherent radiation is the same as that of the primary radiation, the incoherent radiation consists of a continuous spectrum of frequencies—all smaller than the primary frequency—and the probability of interference between two elementary incoherent rays which should have exactly the same frequency is vanishingly small. Intensities, not amplitudes, are therefore added together in the scattering by a molecule, with the result that the angular distribution of the incoherent scattering does not depend upon the relative position of the atoms in the molecule. In the diffraction of X-rays by polyatomic gases, this monotonic background of incoherent intensity is difficult to eliminate experimentally, and it must therefore be taken into account

---

[†] There still exists an effect which is not taken into account by this treatment, namely, the *direct* dependence of the atomic scattering factor upon the frequency of the primary X-rays. See Chapter III.

in the calculation of the scattered intensity. The situation is rather different in the diffraction of X-rays by crystals. In that case the coherent radiation is concentrated in narrow lines which appear on a continuous background, and in principle, at least, the separation of the coherent radiation can be done at once.

THE COMPTON EFFECT

In 1923 Compton[26] studied the spectral distribution of X-rays scattered by graphite, using the apparatus reproduced in Fig. 16. The graphite block R is struck by molybdenum $K\alpha$ radiation ($\lambda = 0.71$ A.) emitted by the tube T. The scattered radiation is analysed by a crystal spectrometer containing an ionization

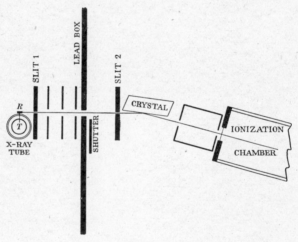

Fig. 16. (After Compton[26].)

chamber. Fig. 17 represents the spectrum of the primary radiation (A) and of the radiation scattered at angles θ equal to $45°$ (B), $90°$ (C) and $135°$ (D). In the secondary radiation there is an undisplaced line P (coherent scattering) and a line M which is broadened and displaced towards the larger wave-lengths (incoherent scattering). The displacement is greater at larger scattering angles; at $\theta = 90°$ it is equal to 0.024 A.

Numerous and accurate experiments have subsequently shown that the magnitude of the displacement does not depend either upon the nature of the scatterer or upon the primary wave-length. The intensity of the displaced line is higher when the scattering element is lighter. Its state of polarization is the same as that of the undisplaced line.

This phenomenon cannot be explained by the classical theory. Compton (25) and Debye (36) have independently given a quantitative theory of the effect, based on quantum mechanics, and according to which the elementary act is a collision between an X-ray photon and an electron. The primary photon of frequency $\nu_0 = c/\lambda_0$ transfers in one step the energy $h\nu_0$ to the electron, formerly at rest (Fig. 18). This energy is quantitatively used, first to create a secondary photon of frequency ν and energy $h\nu$, and secondly to impart to the electron a velocity v. On this basis, a detailed description of the phenomenon can be obtained, using only the laws of conservation of energy and of conservation of momentum, together with the relativistic equivalence between mass and energy. It is found, among other things, that the wave-length displacement of the Compton line is given by the universal formula

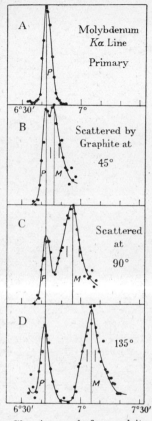

Fig. 17. (After Compton (26).)

$$\lambda - \lambda_0 = 2\Lambda \sin^2 \tfrac{1}{2}\theta, \tag{21}$$

with
$$\Lambda = \frac{h}{mc} = 0.0242 \text{ A.}, \tag{22}$$

λ_0 and λ being respectively the primary and secondary wave-lengths and the other letters having their usual meaning.

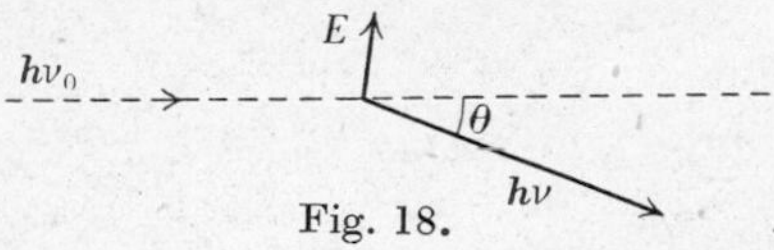

Fig. 18.

ANGULAR DISTRIBUTION OF THE INTENSITY
SCATTERED BY A FREE ELECTRON

Using the above theory, and knowing in what direction a secondary photon is emitted, it is possible to calculate the frequency of the secondary photon as well as the velocity and direction of the recoil electron. The probability of the photon being emitted in a given direction, that is, the angular distribution of the incoherent intensity, is not given, however, by this elementary theory. This intensity distribution has been calculated by Dirac [60] using relativistic quantum mechanics (Heisenberg's method), by Breit [20] using the correspondence principle, and by Gordon [83] using Schrödinger's method. These authors all find that the intensity scattered by a free electron in any direction is $(\nu/\nu_0)^3$ times the Thomson intensity, ν_0 being the primary frequency and ν the secondary frequency in the direction under consideration. The scattered intensity I_s is therefore

$$I_s = I_e\left(\frac{\nu}{\nu_0}\right)^3 = \frac{I_e}{(1+\alpha(1-\cos\theta))^3}, \qquad (23)$$

with
$$\alpha = \frac{\Lambda}{\lambda_0} = \frac{h\nu_0}{mc^2}. \qquad (24)$$

I_e is still used here as a convenient intensity unit, although the intensity I_s in formula (23) represents incoherent intensity, while a Thomson electron would scatter coherent radiation only. For long wave-lengths Λ/λ_0 is small and the angular distribution tends to the classical distribution of intensity. Contrary to what might possibly be expected from a consideration of the elementary theory, the state of polarization of this incoherent radiation is the same as it would be for the case of the Thomson electron.

When γ-rays are scattered by iron, for instance, there is practically no coherent radiation because the wave-length is very short. The energy of the incident photons is large enough for the electrons to be considered as free. The experimental intensity distribution can accordingly be expected to correspond to the distribution given by formula (23). Fig. 19 shows that the agreement is actually much better with this formula than with that of the classical theory.

Calculations have also been made by Klein and Nishina (115) using Dirac's (61) new quantum mechanics, which explains doublet phenomena in terms of the relativity theory and of the general

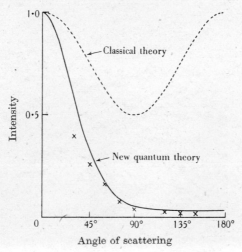

Fig. 19. Variation of the scattered intensity with angle of scattering: (broken line) calculated according to the classical theory; (full line) calculated according to quantum theory by Dirac for $\lambda = 0.022$ A., which makes $\alpha = 1.1$; (crosses) measured by Compton: scattering of γ-rays of the above wave-length by iron. (After Dirac (60).)

theory of transformation in quantum mechanics only. Klein and Nishina give the following formula for the distribution of incoherent intensity:

$$I_s = \frac{I_e}{(1+\alpha(1-\cos\theta))^3}\left[1+\alpha^2\frac{(1-\cos\theta)^2}{(1+\cos^2\theta)(1+\alpha(1-\cos\theta))}\right]. \quad (25)$$

It is the same as formula (23) except for a new term in α^2. This term is negligible for ordinary X-rays, but is important for radiations of very high frequencies. It is supposed to represent radiation which is nearly completely unpolarized.

INCOHERENT SCATTERING BY AN ATOM

Electrons which are completely free scatter only incoherent radiation. On the other hand, it has been seen that electrons in atoms scatter both coherent and incoherent radiation (undisplaced and displaced lines). This is due to the fact that electrons in atoms are not free. For heavy atoms, in which the electrons are more firmly bound, the coherent part of the intensity is relatively greater.

When radiation is scattered coherently, a primary photon of energy $h\nu_0$ is first captured by the atom, and then emitted again in its entirety, the atom falling back to its previous energy level. When radiation is scattered incoherently, part of the primary energy $h\nu_0$ is retained by the atom either to excite or to ionize it, and the photon re-emitted has an energy lower than $h\nu_0$, that is, the scattered radiation has a longer wave-length than the primary radiation.

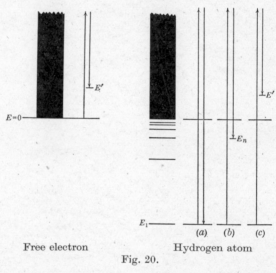

Free electron   Hydrogen atom

Fig. 20.

Hydrogen atom. The energy of a free electron is exclusively of a kinetic nature and can take a continuous series of positive values, starting from zero for the electron at rest (Fig. 20). When a free and resting electron reacts with a photon $h\nu_0$, the electron is momentarily brought to a high energy level, and then falls back to an energy level E', the position of which is a function of the direction taken by the electron. E' being thus the kinetic energy of the recoil electron, $h\nu = h\nu_0 - E'$ is the energy of the photon which is re-emitted. The elementary theory mentioned above gives the relationships between the direction and the energy of the incoherent photon and of the recoil electron.

The case of the hydrogen atom may now be examined. The energy

E of the system can take a series of discrete values corresponding to the stationary states of the atom, the characteristics of which are determined by wave-mechanics. Let the energy scale be chosen so that $E = 0$ for an atom of which the proton and the electron are very far apart, but have no kinetic energy; the stationary energy levels then have negative values. There is also a continuous series of positive levels which correspond to an ionized atom with kinetic energy. When a hydrogen atom in the normal energy state E_1 reacts with a photon $h\nu_0$, one of three things may result (Fig. 20):

(*a*) The atom comes back to its original state with the emission of a coherent photon $h\nu_0$.

(*b*) The atom comes to a stationary state E_n, that is, it remains in an excited state. An incoherent photon is emitted, the energy of which is $h\nu = h\nu_0 - (E_n - E_1)$.

(*c*) The energy of the atom after the reaction is represented by a level in the continuous domain, that is, the atom is ionized and retains a kinetic energy E'. Incoherent radiation of energy $h\nu = h\nu_0 - (E' - E_1)$ is emitted.

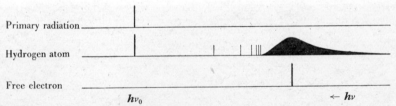

Fig. 21. Schematic representation of the spectrum of the radiation scattered by a hydrogen atom and by a free electron.

The spectrum of the radiation scattered by a hydrogen atom should therefore have the appearance schematically reproduced in Fig. 21: an undisplaced line, a number of discrete Compton lines and a continuous Compton spectrum. The intensity of the different parts of this spectrum depends upon the probability of occurrence of the corresponding atomic process. This has been calculated (173) using wave-mechanics: it is found that the Compton lines are extremely weak[†] and that the continuous region has its maximum intensity

---

† The Compton lines, which are the atomic equivalent of the Raman effect, have not yet been observed experimentally. The intensity distribution in the continuous Compton spectrum has been studied, particularly by DuMond (63, 64), with a view to drawing conclusions as to the movements of electrons in atoms.

precisely where the displaced line would be found according to the elementary theory for the case of a free electron. The spectrum observed in practice accordingly consists of an undisplaced line and of a broadened displaced line.

In the case of coherent scattering, the atom leaves the normal state characterized by the wave-function ψ_1, to come back to the same state ψ_1. The characteristic quantity in the calculations is ψ_1^2, which is interpreted as representing the density of charge in the atom. In the case of incoherent scattering, the atom passes from the state ψ_1 to another state ψ_n. The characteristic quantity then is the product $\psi_1\psi_n$. As far as X-ray diffraction is concerned, however, detailed knowledge of the spectral distribution of the scattered radiation is not necessary. The total intensity, in each direction, of all the components of the incoherent radiation is all that is needed. The mathematical form of the wave-equation *for the hydrogen atom* fortunately happens to be such that this incoherent intensity can be calculated without examining separately all the various products $\psi_1\psi_n$. It can be shown [174, 170] that for this particular atom the total intensity (coherent plus incoherent) scattered in any direction is equal to the intensity scattered by a Thomson electron in the same direction. For unpolarized primary radiation, the value of the incoherent intensity $I_{inc.}$ can be written, therefore, according to equations (3) and (10),

$$I_{inc.} = I_e(1-f_H^2) = I_0 \frac{a_e^2}{R^2} \frac{1+\cos^2\theta}{2}(1-f_H^2), \qquad (26)$$

f_H being the scattering factor for hydrogen defined by equation (15). Fig. 22 shows that the intensity of the incoherent radiation is zero for $\theta = 0$, and increases with increasing $(\sin\frac{1}{2}\theta)/\lambda$ until it constitutes practically the whole of the scattered intensity.

Other atoms. For atoms containing more than one electron, it is impossible to derive the incoherent intensity directly from a knowledge of the atomic scattering factor f, as it is done for hydrogen, because of the absence of the special characteristics of the wave-functions which allow such a procedure to be used.

By analogy with the hydrogen atom, it may be expected that the incoherent intensity of all atoms is zero for $\theta = 0$. On the other hand, for large values of $(\sin\frac{1}{2}\theta)/\lambda$, the coherent scattering of the hydrogen atom disappears and the incoherent intensity is equal to the coherent intensity I_e which would be scattered by a Thomson electron. For an atom containing Z electrons, therefore, it may also be expected that the incoherent intensity will be ZI_e at those angles where the coherent intensity is negligible. As a matter of fact, it is observed experimentally that the total scattered intensity starts from a value proportional to Z^2 and becomes proportional to Z at large values of $(\sin \tfrac{1}{2}\theta)/\lambda$. The manner in which the intensity of the incoherent scattering passes from zero to the limiting value proportional to Z must be calculated. This can be done by various methods.

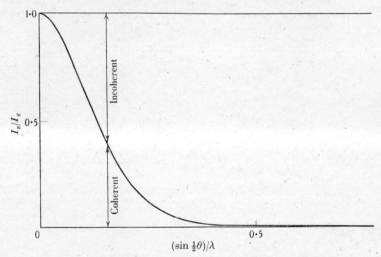

Fig. 22. Coherent and incoherent intensity scattered
by an isolated hydrogen atom.

Heisenberg's method. Heisenberg [94] uses the Thomas-Fermi approximation for the electron distribution in atoms. The mathematical developments are rather difficult, but the same problem has been treated in a way easier to follow by Debye for the case of the free electrons in metals [49]. The idea is the following. When emission of an incoherent photon occurs, an electron takes up the energy difference between the primary and the secondary incoherent photon. It is obviously necessary that the new state of the electron corresponds to an energy level having an empty space, otherwise the process cannot take place. This condition limits the probability of emission of incoherent scattering. An energy level cannot be occupied by more than two electrons (of opposite spin). The deeper the level the more probable it is to find it already occupied. For small angles θ, since the primary photon loses very little energy in favour of the electron, the probability of the electron finding a space in an unoccupied level is very small and it will often return to its initial state, thus allowing coherent, instead of incoherent, radiation to be emitted. Using Fermi's statistics, it is possible to calculate for any scattering angle the proportion of electrons giving incoherent radiation.

While a characteristic atomic radius a, proportional to $Z^{-\frac{1}{3}}$, is used for the calculation of coherent radiation, the characteristic radius for incoherent radiation, b, is proportional to $Z^{-\frac{2}{3}}$. The radius b is given by

$$ b = \frac{1}{Z^{\frac{2}{3}}} \frac{1}{(6\pi)^{\frac{1}{3}}} \left(\frac{3}{32\pi^2}\right)^{\frac{2}{3}} \frac{h^2}{2me^2} = \frac{0 \cdot 176}{Z^{\frac{2}{3}}} \times 10^{-8}\,\text{cm}. \qquad (27) $$

The universal variable used in the calculation is

$$ v = ksb = 4\pi b \frac{\sin \frac{1}{2}\theta}{\lambda}, \qquad (28) $$

and the incoherent intensity scattered by the atom, for unpolarized primary radiation, is

$$ I_{\text{inc.}} = I_0 \frac{a_e^2}{R^2} \frac{1 + \cos^2\theta}{2} ZS(v) = I_e ZS(v), \qquad (29) $$

where $\qquad S(v) = 1 - \displaystyle\int_0^{x_0} x^2 dx \left[\left(\frac{\phi(x)}{x}\right)^{\frac{1}{2}} - v\right]^2 \left[\left(\frac{\phi(x)}{x}\right)^{\frac{1}{2}} + \frac{v}{2}\right].$ (30)

$\phi(x)/x$ is the dimensionless potential used previously in equation (17). The upper limit of integration is defined by $(\phi(x_0)/x_0)^{\frac{1}{2}} - v = 0$.

TABLE II.   *Incoherent scattering function according to Heisenberg-Bewilogua* (10)

$v = ksb$	S	$v = ksb$	S	$v = ksb$	S
0·05	0·319	0·4	0·839	0·8	0·944
0·1	0·486	0·5	0·880	0·9	0·954
0·2	0·674	0·6	0·909	1·0	0·963
0·3	0·776	0·7	0·929		

A numerical table of the values of S as a function of v has been constructed by Bewilogua (10) and is reproduced here (Table II).

In order to obtain the incoherent intensity scattered by an atom, the radius b must first be calculated for this atom using equation (27). For any chosen value of $(\sin \frac{1}{2}\theta)/\lambda$, the quantity v is calculated using equation (28). Table II then gives the corresponding value of S, and the intensity of the incoherent radiation is obtained using equation (29). The incoherent scattering function for argon, given in Fig. 23, has been calculated in this way.

The larger is Z, the smaller is b, and the smaller therefore is S, for any given value of $(\sin \frac{1}{2}\theta)/\lambda$. This means that heavy atoms scatter proportionally less incoherent radiation than light atoms.

Other methods. Heisenberg's method for calculating incoherent scattering is a universal one, immediately applicable to any atom, like the Thomas-Fermi method for calculating coherent scattering. Other methods exist for incoherent, as for coherent, scattering, but in these the case of each atom must be considered separately.

In Hartree's method of calculating the atomic scattering factor f, the separate contributions of the individual electrons are added together. If the scattering factor of the electron i among the Z electrons in the atom is called f_i, the atomic factor f is given by

$$f = \sum_i f_i, \tag{31}$$

where, according to equation (11),

$$f_i = \int_0^\infty \rho_i \, 4\pi r^2 \frac{\sin ksr}{ksr} \, dr, \tag{32}$$

$\rho_i(r)$ representing the probability density of the electron i in the atom. It has been seen above that the use of this method is legitimate. Now equation (26), giving the incoherent scattering for the hydrogen atom, is valid for any other atom containing one electron only. Wentzel[174] applies it successively to each electron i taken separately in the atom:

$$I_{\text{inc.}(i)} = I_e(1 - f_i^2), \tag{33}$$

and takes the sum over all electrons of the atom:

$$I_{\text{inc.}} = I_e \sum_i (1 - f_i^2) = I_e(Z - \sum_i f_i^2). \tag{34}$$

In the same way as the coherent *amplitudes* for each electron were added together to get the coherent amplitude for the atom, the incoherent *intensities* for each electron considered as independent are now added together to get the incoherent intensity scattered by the atom.[†]

Formula (34) is only an approximation because a many-electron problem cannot be expressed as the sum of a number of one-electron problems. To do so would allow each electron independently to make all transitions which are possible in the one-electron problem, and in a system containing several electrons some of these transitions are forbidden because they would lead to a final state which would not obey Pauli's exclusion principle. Waller and Hartree[171,172] treat the problem from this point of view and introduce corrective terms represented here by C:

$$I_{\text{inc.}} = I_e(Z - \sum_i f_i^2 - C). \tag{36}$$

These terms take into account the fact that some components of the incoherent radiation are not emitted, and that the intensity of some other components is altered. The relative importance of these corrections decreases with increasing atomic number Z. Formula (36) probably gives the best numerical values for incoherent intensities when the wave-functions obtained by Hartree's method of the self-consistent field are employed.

Comparison of the methods. The method of Waller-Hartree necessitates a special calculation for each kind of atom. The method of Heisenberg has in practice the considerable advantage of being a universal one. It is therefore interesting to examine its applicability to the study of X-ray diffraction by gases. It has been said above that the Thomas-Fermi approximation becomes unsatisfactory for the calculation of the coherent intensity scattered by light atoms. It must be pointed out, however, that according to

---

[†] Raman[147] and Compton[27], using the classical theory, have given the following formula for the total radiation scattered by an atom:

$$I_{\text{tot.}} = I_e\left(f^2 + Z - \frac{f^2}{Z}\right). \tag{35}$$

The terms $Z - f^2/Z$ have been taken by these authors as representing the incoherent intensity terms, and thus would correspond to the terms $Z - \sum_i f_i^2$ of formula (34).

This is possible only when $f^2 = Z\sum_i f_i^2$, which holds only when all electrons have the same distribution of charge ρ_i in the atom. This actually is true for helium, but it is not so for the other neutral atoms, as Herzog[97] has pointed out. Bewilogua[10] has shown why the apparent verification of equation (35) obtained by Woo[180] using the experimental data of Barrett[2] is not really adequate.

equation (31) the factor f depends in its entirety upon the electron distribution, while equation (36) for incoherent scattering contains a constant term Z, so that errors concerning the electron distribution affect only partially the incoherent intensity terms. As a matter of fact, Bewilogua (10) has shown that Heisenberg's approximation is, for this and other reasons, valid down to the carbon atom $(Z = 6)$.[†] Fig. 23 represents the incoherent intensity for argon

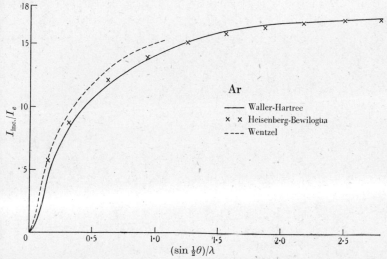

Fig. 23. Incoherent scattering for argon calculated, first, according to Waller-Hartree, using the numerical data published by Herzog (97); secondly, according to Heisenberg-Bewilogua, using Table II; thirdly, according to Wentzel, using the data given by Herzog (98) for $\Sigma_i f_i$.

$(Z = 18)$ according to Waller-Hartree (equation (36)). The approximation of Heisenberg is in good agreement with this curve, especially for high values of the angle variable. At lower values the differences are larger, but it must be borne in mind that, for $(\sin \tfrac{1}{2}\theta)/\lambda = 0\cdot2$, for example, the coherent intensity has a relative value of 159, as against only 6 for the incoherent intensity: an error of 20 % in the latter thus gives an error of less than 1 % in the total intensity. Fig. 21 also shows that the curve according to Wentzel (equation (34)) is in poorer agreement with Waller-Hartree than the Heisenberg curve. Even for neon $(Z = 10)$, the differences between

[†] See also (162).

the Heisenberg and Waller-Hartree methods are small in the range of $(\sin \frac{1}{2}\theta)/\lambda$, where the incoherent intensity is an important part of the total intensity, although in this case the Thomas-Fermi approximation for the scattering factor f is in marked disagreement with that of Hartree.

The incoherent intensity according to Waller-Hartree has been calculated only for helium (99),[†] for neon (98) and for argon (97, 172). But since Heisenberg's method is applicable down to the carbon atom, there remain only the elements Li, Be and B, the incoherent scattering of which is not well known. It would be possible to calculate it, however, since the electron distribution according to Hartree is known (109) for these atoms (by interpolation for Be and B.)[‡]

Relativistic correction. The relativistic correction calculated for free electrons and given by formulae (23) and (25) must also be used for the incoherent scattering of atoms (28). For ordinary X-rays, formula (23) is sufficient. This correction has the effect of reducing the value of the incoherent intensity terms. For instance, using molybdenum radiation ($\lambda = 0\cdot71$ A.), the incoherent radiation is weakened by about 10 % at an angle $\theta = 90°$. Numerical tables of this correction at the different angles θ for different wave-lengths have been calculated by Kaiser (113) and Trieschmann (164). The total intensity scattered by an isolated atom is therefore

$$I_s = I_0 \frac{a_e^2}{R^2} \frac{1 + \cos^2 \theta}{2} [\underset{\text{coherent}}{f^2} + \underset{\text{incoherent}}{QZS}], \qquad (37)$$

where

$$Q = \frac{1}{\left(1 + \dfrac{h(1 - \cos \theta)}{mc\lambda}\right)^3}, \qquad (38)$$

the other letters having their usual meaning. Although the quantities f and S are functions of the variable $(\sin \frac{1}{2}\theta)/\lambda$ alone, this is not true of the whole term between square brackets because the relativistic factor Q depends, not only upon $(\sin \frac{1}{2}\theta)/\lambda$, but also directly upon the wave-length λ.

[†] It seems, however, that the corrective term C of equation (36) has not been taken into consideration here; for the same curve is obtained using equation (34) (numerical values in (28))—or, what in this case is the same, equation (35)—while Waller and Hartree (172) explicitly indicate the existence of this correction for helium.

[‡] Debye (see Bewilogua (10)) has suggested another method which could also be used here, and which consists of representing the electron distribution by hydrogen-like ψ functions.

CHAPTER III

FLUORESCENT RADIATION

WHEN X-rays are scattered by matter, the characteristics of the secondary radiation are closely related to those of the primary radiation and of the scatterer. It has been seen that coherent radiation has the same wave-length as the primary radiation, that it has a definite relation of phase with it, and that its angular distribution directly depends upon the structure of the scattering matter. The properties of the incoherent scattering itself are greatly dependent upon those of the primary radiation. When matter is irradiated with X-rays, however, it also re-emits radiation of quite another type, namely, fluorescent radiation. This is also called characteristic radiation because it has one or several wave-lengths which depend upon the nature of the irradiated *atoms* only. The angular distribution of the fluorescence radiation does not depend upon the direction of the primary radiation or upon the molecular structure of the scatterer.

INTENSITY OF THE CHARACTERISTIC RADIATION

Fluorescence is intimately connected with absorption. An atom absorbs a primary photon, all the energy of which is used up to expel a 'photo-electron' with high kinetic energy from the atom, which therefore remains in an excited state. The primary photon disappears entirely in this process. After a very short time the energy of the excited atom is again liberated, usually by the emission of one or of several fluorescence photons. The energy of these photons depends upon the arrangement of the discrete energy levels of the atom. Thus it does not change steadily when the energy of the incident photon is changed. The probability of emission of these photons is obviously the same for all directions in space. Their emission takes place independently in each atom and no interferences occur.

Now it can also happen that an atom from which a photo-electron has been expelled emits no radiation, but instead expels a second electron from a more peripheral shell (photo-electron of the second kind). This phenomenon constitutes the Auger effect. The probability of an excited atom emitting fluorescence, that is, the ratio of the number of atoms emitting fluorescence to the total number of excited atoms, is called the fluorescence yield. The fluorescence yield is greater for heavy than for light atoms. Fig. 24, after Niens (131), gives the variation of η_K, fluorescence yield for the K radiation, with atomic number Z.

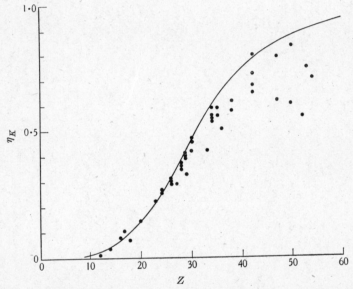

Fig. 24. Dependence of the fluorescence yield η_K upon the atomic number Z. Experimental measurements by various authors (dots) and theoretical curve according to Haas (full line). (After Niens(131).)

The intensity of the fluorescent radiation is considerable in comparison with that of the scattered radiation. As an example, suppose that chlorine is irradiated with copper $K\alpha$ radiation ($\lambda = 1\cdot54\,\mathrm{A.}$), the incident intensity being I_0. At a distance $R = 1$ cm., the intensity scattered at an angle $\theta = 90°$ by a chlorine atom is, disregarding incoherent radiation,

$$I_s = I_0 \frac{a_e^2}{R^2} \frac{1+\cos^2\theta}{2} f_{\mathrm{Cl}(90°)}^2 = I_0 \times 7\cdot9 \times 10^{-26} \times \tfrac{1}{2} \times (7\cdot57)^2$$
$$= 2\cdot26 \times 10^{-24} \times I_0. \tag{39}$$

On the other hand, after passing through a layer of chlorine containing 1 g./cm.^{2} area, the intensity of the primary radiation is diminished to a value $I_0 e^{-\mu/\rho}$. The mass absorption coefficient μ/ρ (μ linear absorption coefficient, ρ density) is in the present case equal to 103·4 (18). If now μ/ρ is divided by the number N of atoms contained in 1 g. chlorine, the result is the absorption coefficient per atom. The mean intensity of radiation absorbed by one chlorine atom is thus

$$I_0 - I_0 e^{-\mu/\rho N} = I_0(1 - e^{6\cdot0 \times 10^{-21}}) \approx 6\cdot0 \times 10^{-21} \times I_0. \qquad (40)$$

The fluorescence yield for chlorine is about 0·1; taking into account that the energy of the incident photons ($\lambda = 1\cdot54$ A.) is higher than that of the fluorescence photons ($\lambda = 4\cdot7$ A.), the mean fluorescent intensity for a chlorine atom at a distance $R = 1$ cm. is found to be

$$I_{\text{fl.}} = I_0 \times 6\cdot0 \times 10^{-21} \times 0\cdot1 \times \frac{1\cdot54}{4\cdot7} \times \frac{1}{4\pi} = 1\cdot56 \times 10^{-23} \times I_0. \qquad (41)$$

Comparison with formula (39) shows that fluorescence is here almost seven times as intense as scattered radiation.

Since X-rays of short wave-length are less absorbed than those of long wave-length, their use reduces the intensity of fluorescence, but it does not suppress it. Fluorescence remains in practice an intense parasitic radiation, the intensity of which cannot be accurately calculated. It must therefore be eliminated experimentally. As the fluorescence wave-length is different from the primary wave-length, this can generally be done using selective absorption filters. In the case of heavy atoms, the K radiation may be too hard for this procedure to be practicable. A primary radiation may then be used, the wave-length of which is longer than that of the K absorption edge of the atoms, which under these conditions emit only the softer $L, M, \ldots$ fluorescence. It must be borne in mind, however, that the above theories for the coherent and incoherent scattering are then no longer strictly valid, because they assume that the primary frequency is appreciably higher than all characteristic frequencies of the atom.

DEPENDENCE OF ATOMIC SCATTERING FACTOR
UPON WAVE-LENGTH

When X-ray frequencies are used which are only slightly higher than the K critical frequency of the atom, the amplitude scattered by the K electrons is increased by resonance. Changes of phase also occur. The interferences between the radiation scattered by the K electrons and by the other electrons then result in a decrease of the total amplitude, so that the atomic scattering factor becomes considerably smaller. For frequencies slightly lower than the critical atomic frequency, on the other hand, the factor f increases again. It then remains below its value at high frequencies, however, because the K electrons no longer take part in the scattering.

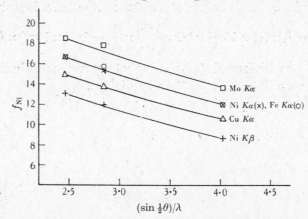

Fig. 25. Measurements of the atomic scattering factor of nickel for various wave-lengths. (After Jesse (112).)

Hönl (104, 103) has given a wave-mechanical theory of this pheno-menon. It is a problem of the general theory of dispersion of light. The first result concerns the quantity, Δf, defined by

$$\Delta f = f_{\lambda \to 0} - f_\lambda, \tag{42}$$

where f_λ is the atomic scattering factor for a wave-length λ, and $f_{\lambda \to 0}$ is the factor for wave-lengths so short that dispersion effects are negligible. For a given wave-length, the value of Δf is practically independent of θ, that is, the curves giving in terms of $(\sin \frac{1}{2}\theta)/\lambda$ the factors f for different wave-lengths are all parallel. As shown in Fig. 25, this receives experimental confirmation from measurements by Jesse (112) on nickel. The theory also gives the variation of Δf itself with the wave-length. Fig. 26 shows that there is general agreement between theory and experiment, although this agreement is not quantitative for some of the points on the long wave-length side.[†]

In X-ray diffraction, it follows that the use of primary frequencies very near the critical frequencies of the atoms is to be avoided. Frequencies higher than the critical frequencies are preferable, whenever possible. For heavy atoms the use of such wave-lengths may not be practicable; the atomic scattering factor then can still be calculated, although with a lower accuracy.

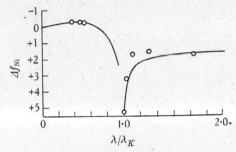

Fig. 26. Measurements of Δf for nickel (circles), compared with Hönl's theory (full line). (After Jesse (112).)

The conditions of validity of the calculation of incoherent intensity according to Waller-Hartree or Heisenberg are the same as those for the calculation of the coherent intensity according to Hartree or Thomas-Fermi. An error is therefore made when the incoherent intensity is calculated by the usual method and an X-ray frequency lower than the atomic critical frequency is used. As this occurs mainly for heavy atoms, however, the error on the total scattered intensity is relatively small.

† For details see (112) and (1).

CHAPTER IV

EXPERIMENTAL MEASUREMENTS OF THE SCATTERING OF X-RAYS BY ATOMS

MONATOMIC GASES

THE measurement of the diffraction of X-rays by monatomic gases gives directly the intensity of the radiation scattered by free atoms. Although it is possible to separate experimentally the coherent from the incoherent scattering, it is the total intensity scattered by gases which has generally been measured. In this chapter, only brief mention of the experimental techniques will be made; more detail will be found in Chapter XII.

After unsuccessful attempts by other investigators, Barrett[2], in 1928, determined the scattering function of argon, that is, the intensity as a function of the scattering angle, using an ionization chamber. Excess scattering was observed at small angles. The proof that this effect was really due to interferences inside the atom was given by the fact that the excess scattering appeared at larger angles when longer wave-lengths were used. 'White' radiation of short wave-length was used. In the same year, Scherrer and Stäger[154] published photographic measurements of the scattering by mercury vapour (Fig. 27). Mercury was chosen, among other reasons, because it is heavy enough to permit the incoherent radiation to be neglected. The chief result of the experiments is that they give for the atomic scattering factor of mercury a curve presenting neither maxima nor minima, and thus similar to the monotonic curves of the atomic factors derived from measurements on crystals (Fig. 28). The authors estimate that the accuracy of their measured intensities is probably not better than about $\pm 10 \%$. The filtered primary radiation (Cu $K\alpha$) is incapable of exciting the K fluorescence of mercury. The f curve calculated by the Thomas-Fermi approximation, although valid only for a primary frequency higher than the critical K frequency, nevertheless is in good agreement with experiment, as shown in Fig. 28. In this connexion it must be borne in mind that the slope of the curve is small. Again, the intensity measurements are not absolute measurements: the scale was adjusted in such a way that the ordinates of the experimental and theoretical curves coincide at $\theta = 90°$. Remembering that the error $\varDelta f$ in the scattering factor must be the same at all angles, the agreement observed then becomes understandable.

Wollan[176], using an ionization chamber, studied in 1931 the diffraction by helium, neon and argon. Molybdenum radiation $(\lambda = 0.71\,\mathrm{A}.)$ was used, with (except for helium) 'balanced filters'

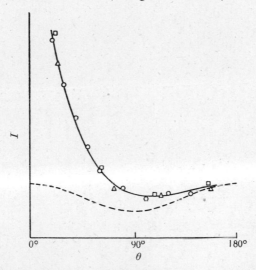

Fig. 27. Experimental measurement of the X-ray intensity scattered by mercury vapour according to Scherrer and Stäger, for a wave-length of 1·54 A.

The dotted line below represents the theoretical angular distribution of intensity, proportional to the polarization factor $(1+\cos^2\theta)/2$, which would be given by a classical resonator such as a Thomson electron. Comparison with Fig. 28 shows that it is the polarization factor which is the cause of the minimum observed in the experimental intensity curve at about $\theta = 120°$. (After Scherrer and Stäger[154].)

which give a good monochromatization. All intensities were measured by comparison with the intensity scattered by hydrogen at an angle of 90°, which can be calculated considering the two atoms of the hydrogen molecule as independent. Wollan therefore considers these measurements to be absolute measurements, but it must be remarked that the hydrogen measurements were made without filters, and subsequently corrected in a particular way.[†]

† See (98).

In the same year, Herzog[97] measured photographically the diffraction by argon gas of filtered copper radiation ($\lambda = 1\cdot54$ A.). This measurement is of special interest, because the same author[100], using the same diffraction cell, succeeded in 1933 in making an absolute measurement of the diffraction by this gas, that is, in comparing directly the intensity scattered by the gas with the intensity of the incident beam. The primary intensity being some ten million times greater than the scattered intensity, the experimental technique had to be pushed to its extreme limit. The in-

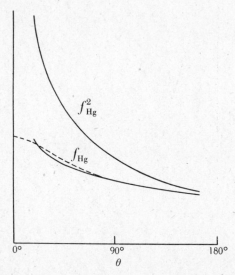

Fig. 28. Experimental values of f^2 and f for mercury.

The curve f^2 has been obtained by dividing the intensity values of Fig. 27 by the polarization factor, the incoherent intensity being neglected. (After Scherrer and Stäger[154].)

The broken line which has been added in the present figure represents the values of f calculated according to Thomas and Fermi, using Table I. The ordinates of the two f curves, experimental and theoretical, have been made to coincide at $\theta = 90°$.

tensity scattered at an angle of $40°$ and the primary intensity were measured with the same ionization chamber. By using balanced filters, results referring to monochromatic radiation were obtained. The calculation of the total scattering according to Waller-Hartree[172] and the measurement of the geometrical dimensions of the apparatus gave a theoretical value of the ratio R of the scattered energy to the primary energy: $R_{calc.} = 2 \cdot 87 \times 10^{-7} \pm 6\,\%$. The measured value, $R_{exp.} = 2 \cdot 88 \times 10^{-7} \pm 5\,\%$, is in excellent agreement with the calculations. The incoherent intensity in the present case is only of the order of $1\,\%$: it is therefore really the Hartree method for calculating f which receives confirmation from these measurements.

The relative measurements by Herzog were in agreement with the theory of Waller-Hartree, while the new measurements prove that agreement also exists for the absolute values of the whole curve. Fig. 29 represents the calculated curve and the experi-

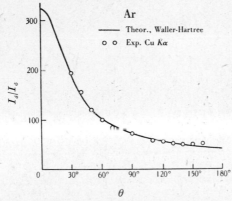

Fig. 29. X-ray scattering by argon. Measurements by Herzog for $\lambda = 1 \cdot 54$ A. (After Herzog (97).)

mental points. Fig. 30 gives as function of $(\sin \tfrac{1}{2}\theta)/\lambda$ the calculated coherent and incoherent intensities for argon. The measurements are in agreement with the theory, not only at angles where the scattering is nearly exclusively coherent, but also where the incoherent intensity is an appreciable part of the total intensity. Wollan's measurements on argon,[†] made using a shorter wavelength ($\lambda = 0 \cdot 71$ A.), also agree with the theory (98) as shown by Fig. 31. (It is not possible to compare these various measurements with one and the same theoretical curve, because the relativistic correction of incoherent scattering depends upon the wave-length.) Monochromatic measurements on neon made by Wollan (176) are also in agreement with the theory (98).

† On the diffraction of X-rays by argon, see also (69).

The case of helium is especially interesting because of the high intensity of the incoherent radiation scattered by this gas, as shown in Fig. 32. Wollan's measurements on helium unfortunately had to be made using unfiltered radiation and were corrected afterwards. The agreement with theory nevertheless is satisfactory (99), as shown in Fig. 33. In that figure the theoretical curve is drawn using the

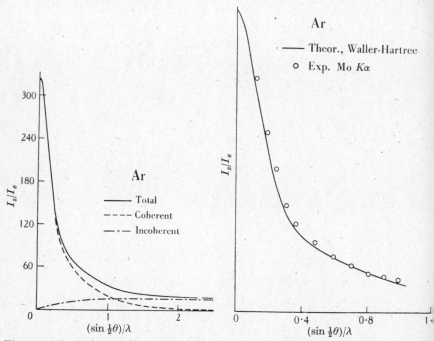

Fig. 30. Theoretical X-ray scattering by argon according to Waller-Hartree. (After Herzog (97).)

Fig. 31. X-ray scattering by argon. Measure ments by Wollan, for $\lambda = 0.71$ A. (After Herzog (98).)

relativistic correction, and also without it. Since at large angles the scattered intensity is nearly exclusively incoherent, the agreement of the measurements with the curve using the relativistic correction proves the validity of this correction.[†]

Compton (27) has shown that, knowing the angular distribution of the coherent intensity, it is possible to calculate the electron distribution in the atom by using Fourier analysis. The incoherent

[†] For measurements of the ratio of coherent to incoherent intensity, see (179).

intensity must generally be eliminated by calculation, since it cannot be expressed as a function of the atomic scattering factor f, and some extrapolations are necessary, because the scattered intensity cannot be measured for all values of $(\sin \frac{1}{2}\theta)/\lambda$. Electron distribution in satisfactory agreement with Hartree's theoretical distributions have been obtained: for neon, the shells K and L are

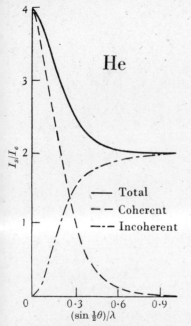

Fig. 32. Theoretical X-ray scattering by helium, according to Waller-Hartree. (After Herzog(99).)

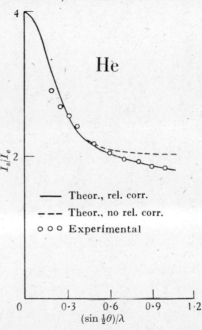

Fig. 33. X-ray scattering by helium. The circles represent measurements by Wollan, for $\lambda = 0.71$ A. The full line represents the Waller-Hartree theoretical curve with the relativistic correction of the incoherent intensity for the above wave-length. (After Herzog(99).)

resolved(177) in the electron distribution calculated in this way. According to Herzog(97), however, this Fourier method may in practice give rise to not inconsiderable errors. It seems preferable to determine the electron distribution by a method of trial and error: assuming a theoretical distribution, calculating the scattering function corresponding to it, and comparing the latter with observation. It is, of course, this procedure which has been used above in order to verify Hartree's calculations. When the method of trial and error is chosen, the calculations are based on assumed theoretical data which can be quite complete. These therefore can then be accurately verified within the experimental range, which is always necessarily limited. When Fourier analysis is used, on the contrary, the calculations must be based on experimental data, which perforce are incomplete.

CRYSTALS

As has been pointed out, the coherent radiation in the case of crystals becomes automatically separated, and, knowing the Bragg reflexion intensities, it is possible to calculate the atomic scattering factor of the constituents of the crystal. In practice these determinations are delicate as much from the theoretical as from the experimental standpoint, because thermal vibrations in the crystal appreciably weaken the intensities, and because various correction factors determined by the perfection of the crystal structure (mosaic crystals) must be taken into account. Absolute measurements of atomic factors in crystals have been made chiefly by the Bragg school.[†] Upon this important question the reader is referred to the review articles of James (111), of Wollan (178), and of Ehrenberg and Schäfer (65). The latter contains a table of atomic factor measurements. The agreement found between the most precise measurements and theory gives support to the accuracy of the Hartree scattering factors and to the theory of the temperature effect in crystals.

It is in general easier to obtain elements in the atomic state in crystals than in gases; this constitutes an advantage in using crystals in the measurement of atomic scattering factors. It must be pointed out, however, that crystal measurements become in principle impossible below a certain value of $(\sin \frac{1}{2}\theta)/\lambda$, given by the Bragg reflexion condition

$$2d \sin \tfrac{1}{2}\theta = n\lambda,\text{[‡]} \tag{43}$$

[†] See for example (107).

[‡] As has been pointed out above, θ represents here the angle between primary and scattered rays. Our $\frac{1}{2}\theta$ therefore corresponds to the angle of the primary ray with the reflecting plane, which is called θ by Bragg. Crystallographers generally use the notation 2θ for the angle which throughout this book is called θ.

where d is the spacing and n is a positive integer number. For a given spacing d, no reflexion can occur for

$$\frac{\sin \frac{1}{2}\theta}{\lambda} < \frac{1}{2d}. \tag{44}$$

In the X-ray diffraction by gases, on the contrary, there is no difficulty in principle in extending the measurements to small scattering angles, which are specially useful for obtaining knowledge of the outer electrons of the atom. The fact that no correction is necessary for thermal motion and for various other factors is also an important advantage of the diffraction by monatomic gases.

The intensity scattered by gases changes progressively with angle, so that when the primary radiation contains two different wave-lengths, the smooth patterns corresponding to the different wave-lengths become superposed and cannot be separated. In the case of crystals, on the other hand, the scattered intensity, apart from the continuous background, appears in sharp monochromatic lines. The two methods therefore differ greatly from the experimental point of view. They are complementary to one another, but it is scarcely possible to compare their results, because the elements which are easy to study as monatomic gases are usually difficult to study as atomic crystals, and vice versa.

It has hitherto been supposed that the electron distribution in atoms is spherically symmetrical. Strictly speaking this is likely to be inexact, at least for the outer electron shells. If this error were noticeable, the factor f should depend not only upon $(\sin \frac{1}{2}\theta)/\lambda$, that is, on the scattering angle θ, but also upon the orientation of the atom relative to the incident radiation. In a monatomic gas this effect obviously cannot be verified, because only the mean of the intensity for all orientations of the atoms is observable. On the other hand, non-symmetrical atoms in a crystal would certainly be regularly orientated throughout the lattice, and here the kind of averaging which takes place in the case of gases would not occur. The atoms therefore could be orientated at will relative to the primary beam simply by orientating the crystal as a whole. Now if two different sets of planes in the crystal happen to have identical spacings, measurements of the atomic scattering factor f, for the same value of the scattering angle θ, can be made in turn for these two sets of planes—that is, for two different orientations of the atoms relative to the incident radiation. Two different values of f might thus be found for the same value of the scattering angle θ. Such differences, however, have not been observed outside the limits of experimental error.

It may also happen that the structure of a crystal is such that certain reflexions are 'forbidden'. This means that, provided the atoms are spherically symmetrical, these reflexions must have zero amplitude. Actual occurrence of such reflexions therefore must be an indication of the lack of spherical symmetry in the atoms in the crystal. It is clear that the existence of forbidden reflexions must be easier to detect than the existence of the variations in the value of f which have just been mentioned. A forbidden reflexion is observed in the case of diamond. The properties of the diamond lattice are such that reflexion 222 cannot appear if the electron distribution in the diamond atoms is spherically symmetrical. Now this forbidden reflexion is observed with a small but accurately measurable intensity. This therefore shows with certainty that the atoms in diamonds are not spherical. The concentration of electrons in the chemical bond must evidently account for this deviation from spherical symmetry. A wave-mechanical treatment of the theoretical problem has been given by Ewald and Hönl[71] and measurements have been published by Renninger[150]. The observed intensity of the 222 reflexion is of the order of magnitude expected from the theoretical calculation—although actually greater—and reflexion 622, another forbidden reflexion which the theory predicts to be extremely weak, is actually not observed.[†]

The incoherent intensity scattered by crystals is not precisely equal to the continuous background, because this background contains also coherent radiation. According to Debye[31], the sharp lines of coherent radiation are, on account of the thermal vibrations in the crystal, accompanied by a diffuse scattering which is greater the more the line intensity is reduced. No direct measurement of

---

[†] On the structure of diamond see also (21).

incoherent intensity is therefore possible for crystals.[†] It may be pointed out that it has been found that the diffuse background due to thermal vibrations in the crystal is not structureless as the early theory of Debye [31] predicts, but contains more or less well-defined spots and streamers.[‡]

[†] See (178) and (65). The scattering due to thermal vibrations is in general treated as coherent, but, actually, it consists of radiation which is slightly incoherent because the incoming quantum has been changed by giving some of its energy to the thermal vibrations.

[‡] See e.g. (14) and the reviews (119) and (15). This structure of the background is determined by the characteristics of the vibrations occurring in the crystal and thus can give important information about the dynamics of the crystal lattice.

CHAPTER V

DIFFRACTION OF FAST ELECTRONS BY ATOMS

THE diffraction of fast electrons by gases, discovered in 1930 by Mark and Wierl (122), has acquired great importance as a method of determining molecular structures, especially as developed by Pauling and his school.† Its fundamental principle is the same as that of X-ray diffraction by gases.

COHERENT SCATTERING

When a parallel beam of electrically charged particles enters the field of force of an atom, the particles are deflected from their original path and the beam is diffracted. The scattered intensity may be defined in the following way. Suppose the incident beam sends a number I_0 of particles through unit area in unit time: I_0 is then the primary intensity. The diffracting centre being at the point O, suppose a disk of area ds to be situated at a point P at a distance R from O, R being large compared with atomic dimensions. The direction OP makes an angle θ with the direction of the primary beam and the disk ds is normal to OP. Then, if $I_s ds$ is the number of particles striking the disk per unit time, I_s is by definition the intensity scattered at the angle θ at the distance R.

According to wave-mechanics, a beam of particles travelling all with the same velocity can be represented by a wave, the wavelength λ of which is given by the relation of Louis de Broglie, which is written, disregarding the relativistic correction,

$$\lambda = \frac{h}{mv}, \qquad (45)$$

where h is Planck's constant, m is the mass and v the velocity of the particles. The square of the amplitude of this associated wave is the intensity of the beam. When the beam is diffracted by a system of several points, interferences occur on account of the wave-nature

† See the review articles by Brockway (22) and Maxwell (187).

of the beam. There is not a mere superposition of the angular distributions of intensity which are to be expected for each centre taken separately. It is, on the contrary, the amplitudes, not the intensities, which are added together, exactly as in the case of the diffraction of electro-magnetic radiation.

If an electron beam, the associated wave of which has an amplitude A_0, and a wave-length λ, falls into the electrostatic field of an atom of atomic number Z, the scattered wave, according to wave-mechanical theory (129), has an amplitude A_s equal to

$$A_s = \frac{A_0}{R} \frac{8\pi^2 me^2}{h^2} F = \frac{A_0}{R} \frac{2}{a_H} F, \tag{46}$$

where
$$F = \frac{Z-f}{\left(4\pi \dfrac{\sin \frac{1}{2}\theta}{\lambda}\right)^2}, \tag{47}$$

m being the electron mass, $-e$ the electron charge, and h Planck's constant. F is called the atomic scattering factor for electrons. The function f is the scattering factor of the atom for X-rays of the same wave-length λ. The intensity I_s scattered by the isolated atom is therefore

$$I_s = A_s^2 = \frac{I_0}{R^2} \frac{4}{a_H^2} F^2. \tag{48}$$

The limits of validity of this formula are the same as those of the calculation of X-ray coherent scattering. The incident electrons must have an energy higher than the binding energy of the K electrons of the atom. This sets an upper limit of, say, 0·1 A. to the electron wave-lengths which can be used.[†] X-rays of much longer wave-lengths correspond to the same energy.

Thus the electron scattering factor F is obtained immediately from a knowledge of the X-ray factor f. Like the latter, F is a function of $(\sin \frac{1}{2}\theta)/\lambda$. It contains a positive term in Z which is due to the action of the positively charged nucleus, and a negative term

[†] In terms of the accelerating potential V in volts, the electron wave-length λ is given, in Ångström units, by

$$\lambda = \sqrt{\frac{150}{V}}. \tag{49}$$

For the relativistic correction, see Thomson (163), 3rd ed., vol. 2, p. 28.

in $-f$ which represents the screening effect of the electron atmosphere.

Equation (48) can also be written

$$I_s = \frac{I_0}{R^2}\left(\frac{e^2}{2mv^2}\right)^2 \frac{(Z-f)^2}{\sin^4 \frac{1}{2}\theta}, \tag{50}$$

where mv^2 is twice the energy of each of the electrons. If in this formula f is made equal to zero, an angular distribution proportional to $Z^2(\sin \frac{1}{2}\theta)^{-4}$ is obtained. This is the well-known distribution observed by Rutherford in the diffraction of α-particles by atomic nuclei.

The coherent X-ray intensity scattered by an isolated atom has been found above to be represented by equation (10); it can be rewritten

$$\text{X-rays:} \quad I_s = \frac{1+\cos^2\theta}{2}\frac{I_0}{R^2}a_e^2 f^2. \tag{51}$$

For electron rays, the equation is

$$\text{Electrons:} \quad I_s = \frac{I_0}{R^2}\frac{4}{a_H^2}\frac{(Z-f)^2}{\left(4\pi\dfrac{\sin \frac{1}{2}\theta}{\lambda}\right)^4}; \tag{52}$$

there is no polarization factor in this case. Using these equations the ratios of the scattered to the primary intensity for the case of X-rays and for the case of electrons may be compared. The factor $4\pi(\sin \frac{1}{2}\theta)/\lambda$ may be taken equal, for instance, to 10, λ being expressed in A. The values of a_e and a_H are respectively $2\cdot8 \times 10^{-5}$ and $0\cdot53$ A. Equations (51) and (52) then become

$$\text{X-rays:} \quad \frac{I_s}{I_0} = \frac{1}{R^2}\frac{1+\cos^2\theta}{2}(2\cdot8 \times 10^{-5})^2 f^2 \approx 10^{-9} \times \frac{f^2}{R^2}, \tag{53}$$

$$\text{Electrons:} \quad \frac{I_s}{I_0} = \frac{1}{R^2}\frac{4}{(0\cdot53)^2}\frac{(Z-f)^2}{10^4} \approx 10^{-3} \times \frac{(Z-f)^2}{R^2}. \tag{54}$$

The quantities f and $(Z-f)$ being of the same order of magnitude, this means that the interaction with matter is of the order of a million times greater in the case of electrons than in the case of X-rays. This explains why, when photographic recording is used, the times of exposure are of the order of magnitude of only a second for electrons, while for X-rays they last hours. The electron intensity, however, decreases very rapidly with increasing $(\sin \tfrac{1}{2}\theta)/\lambda$ because this variable occurs with the fourth power in the denominator of formula (52), and at large angles the electron interaction becomes as small as that of X-rays[145].

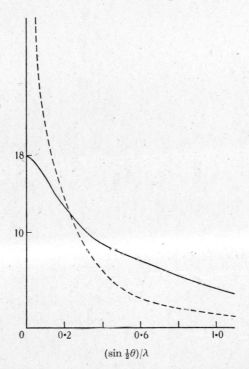

Fig. 34. The X-ray and electron scattering factors for the argon atom. Full line: f; broken line: $F \times (4\pi)^2/10$. (After Pirenne[145].)

As shown in Fig. 34, for the case of argon, both the f and the F factors decrease with increasing $(\sin \tfrac{1}{2}\theta)/\lambda$. The decrease, at least at the beginning of the curve, is more rapid for F, on account of the factor $[(\sin \tfrac{1}{2}\theta)/\lambda]^{-2}$ in formula (47). An important difference between electron and X-ray diffraction is that, when this fast-decreasing factor is disregarded, the characteristic quantity for electrons is $(Z - f)$, while it is f for X-rays. The latter quantity tends to zero for large values of $(\sin \tfrac{1}{2}\theta)/\lambda$, while $(Z - f)$ tends to Z under the same conditions.

INCOHERENT SCATTERING

An atom can react with an X-ray photon and remain in an excited state, a photon being re-emitted with an energy lower than that of the primary one. In the same way, an atom having reacted with a rapid electron can be left at an energy level higher than the initial one, the electron suffering a corresponding loss of energy. Electrons scattered in this way display a whole spectrum of velocities. Their associated waves have various wave-lengths for any given scattering angle. They constitute the incoherent part of the scattered intensity, while the coherent part corresponds to processes following which the atom returns to its initial state. Morse (128) has calculated that the total intensity scattered by an atom is

$$I_s = \frac{I_0}{R^2}\frac{4}{a_H^2}\left[\underset{\text{coherent}}{\frac{(Z-f)^2}{\left(4\pi\dfrac{\sin\frac{1}{2}\theta}{\lambda}\right)^4}} + \underset{\text{incoherent}}{\frac{ZS}{\left(4\pi\dfrac{\sin\frac{1}{2}\theta}{\lambda}\right)^4}}\right]. \tag{55}$$

The first term between brackets represents coherent scattering; it has been given above in equation (52). The second term represents incoherent scattering. S is the incoherent scattering function calculated for X-rays by Heisenberg and given by equation (30). The first main difference between equation (55) for electron and equation (37) of Chapter II for X-ray diffraction is the existence in the former of the factor $[(\sin\frac{1}{2}\theta)/\lambda]^{-4}$, giving rise to a rapid decrease of intensity with increasing angle, and which affects the incoherent as well as the coherent intensity term. The other difference concerns the behaviour of the coherent and incoherent intensity terms. At increasing values of $(\sin\frac{1}{2}\theta)/\lambda$ in the case of electrons, the coherent term tends to become proportional to Z^2, and the incoherent term to Z: the coherent term therefore always retains a great relative importance. In the case of X-rays, on the other hand, the coherent term tends to zero while the incoherent term tends to Z, the incoherent term therefore becoming predominant.

EXPERIMENTAL MEASUREMENTS

Mark and Wierl (123) have measured the relative intensities of the rings of Debye-Scherrer patterns obtained when electrons are diffracted by thin (10^{-6} cm.) microcrystalline foils of aluminium, silver and gold. The angular distribution of the coherent scattered intensity has also been calculated theoretically. Fig. 35 represents the experimental points together with the calculated curves and the Rutherford distribution. Although incoherent scattering has not been taken into account, the agreement is fairly good; it is least satisfactory for aluminium, an element for which the incoherent intensity should be important. The figure shows that the heavier the atom the more the intensity distribution differs from the Rutherford distribution. The experiments have also confirmed that heavy atoms scatter much more intensely than light atoms.[†]

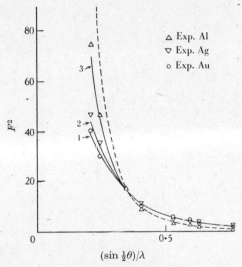

Fig. 35. Theoretical electron scattering for gold (1), for silver (2), and for aluminium (3). Rutherford scattering function (broken line). Experimental measurements of the scattered intensity by Mark and Wierl. The ordinates of the curves have all been made equal at a particular value of the abscissa, where they are seen to cross one another. (After Mark and Wierl (123).)

For electron scattering by monatomic gases (105, 118, 121) there is not as much satisfactory experimental verification as for X-ray scattering. But the above theory receives support from the results of the careful electron diffraction studies which have been made of some polyatomic gases, such as carbon tetrachloride (58).

[†] See, however, the different results reported in (133) and (12). The problem of the scattering of electrons by thin metallic foils is a complicated one, on which many papers have been published in the last few years.

CHAPTER VI

DIFFRACTION OF X-RAYS BY FREE MOLECULES

GENERAL

THE discovery of X-ray interferences in crystals, made in 1912 by von Laue, Friedrich and Knipping(78), showed that the wavelength of X-rays is short enough to make possible the measurement of atomic and molecular dimensions. If the molecules to be studied in this way are free, however, the investigator is faced with the difficulty of dealing with particles which cannot, like a crystal, be kept in a fixed orientation in space. Fortunately, as has been explained in Chapter I, it was found that a rigid system of diffracting points must show recognizable interferences in the radiation it scatters, even if the system changes continually and in an uncontrollable way its orientation in space. Debye was being led by this theoretical consideration when, in 1916, he discovered with Scherrer the X-ray interferences given by crystal powders(33,35) and liquids(34). These experiments were forerunners to the investigation made in 1928 by Debye, Bewilogua and Ehrhardt(39,40), which was the first to show interference rings in the diffraction of X-rays by a gas, namely, by carbon tetrachloride, CCl_4, in the vapour state.

In fact, the diffraction of X-rays by gases is very similar to the diffraction by crystal powders, for each small crystal can be considered as one large molecule, the interatomic forces in crystals being not essentially different from the interatomic forces which build up molecules. Crystals, even when small, are 'molecules' which contain large numbers of regularly distributed atoms, and therefore give sharp interference patterns. For this reason it is more easily understandable in the case of crystals than in the case of gases that interferences remain visible in the diffraction pattern even when the particles are oriented at random.

It was thought at first that the structure of free molecules could be determined from the scattering function of substances in the liquid state, but this is not so. For strong interference effects exist between molecules and molecules in the liquid, which, moreover, retains some kind of intermolecular organization, the molecules, for instance, being unable to rotate freely. It was therefore necessary to investigate gases, despite experimental difficulties. Gases are truly amorphous substances, and each gas molecule scatters very nearly in the same way as it would if entirely isolated.

The choice of carbon tetrachloride for the first successful gas diffraction experiments was not due to chance. Previous attempts to show interference effects in X-ray diffraction by polyatomic gases had remained unsuccessful because the molecules and the experimental conditions had not been suitably chosen [9]. The CCl_4 molecule was chosen because the theory predicted well-marked maxima in its scattering curve on account of the six equal distances between the heavy chlorine atoms in the supposedly tetrahedral molecule. The expected maxima were found and a preliminary value of 3 A. for the Cl-Cl distance was deduced from their position. Subsequent investigations on CCl_4, which became a kind of 'standard' molecule for diffraction experiments, have shown a remarkable agreement between the whole intensity curve and theoretical calculations, at the same time demonstrating the regular tetrahedral structure of the molecule.

USE OF ATOMIC SCATTERING FACTORS

The angular distribution of the intensity scattered by an actual molecule, free and isolated in space, must now be calculated. As has been seen in Chapter I, the angular distribution of the mean coherent intensity $\bar{I}_s$ scattered by an undeformable system of Thomson electrons $1, 2, \ldots, i, \ldots, j, \ldots, n$, the system taking all possible orientations in space with equal probabilities, is given [32] by the following equation:

$$\bar{I}_s = I_e \sum_i \sum_j \frac{\sin x_{ij}}{x_{ij}}, \tag{56}$$

where

$$I_e = I_0 \frac{a_e^2}{R^2} \frac{1 + \cos^2 \theta}{2}, \tag{57}$$

and

$$x_{ij} = 4\pi l_{ij} \frac{\sin \frac{1}{2}\theta}{\lambda}, \tag{58}$$

l_{ij} being the distance between the electrons i and j in the system.

This formula, obtained for diffracting *points*, can be extended to diffracting systems having a continuous structure, such as the charge cloud of a molecule:

$$\bar{I}_s = I_e \iint \rho_1 \rho_2 \frac{\sin x_{12}}{x_{12}} dV_1 dV_2. \tag{59}$$

ρ_1 and ρ_2 are the electron densities in volume elements dV_1 and dV_2 situated at a mutual distance r_{12}, and

$$x_{12} = 4\pi r_{12} \frac{\sin \frac{1}{2}\theta}{\lambda}. \tag{60}$$

The calculation of the above integral for electron atmospheres of irregular shapes would be very intricate in practice, but a great simplification can usually be achieved in the following way. *The electron atmosphere of the whole molecule is considered as being made up of the atmospheres of the various atoms which constitute it, these atmospheres being merely juxtaposed one to another, and each of them remaining spherically symmetrical.* The validity of this assumption is discussed in Chapter IX. For spherically symmetrical atoms, and in this case only, the amplitude scattered at a given angle is independent of the orientation of the atoms relative to the primary beam. According to the above representation of the molecule, *each atom can therefore be replaced in the calculations by a point, the scattering power of which is, on the Thomson scale, different for every angle θ.* The scattering power of this point is in fact equal to the scattering factor f of the atom, for f represents the amplitude scattered by this atom relative to the amplitude scattered by a Thomson electron, which is taken as unity. Thus, if the system which scatters X-rays, instead of being made of n point electrons, is a molecule constituted of n spherically symmetrical atoms $1, 2, ..., i, ..., j, ..., n$, formula (56) must be replaced (44) by

$$\bar{I}_s = I_e \sum_i \sum_j f_i f_j \frac{\sin x_{ij}}{x_{ij}}, \tag{61}$$

x_{ij} being given by equation (58), where l_{ij} is now an *interatomic* distance.

INFLUENCE OF ATOMIC SIZE ON THE MOLECULAR SCATTERING FUNCTION

Theoretical. The atomic scattering factors f in equation (61) take into account the number of electrons contained in the atom as well as their distribution in the atom. The chief characteristic with regard to the latter is the atomic size, that is, the dimensions of the volume around the nucleus in which the major part of the charge cloud is concentrated. The larger and the more diffuse the charge cloud, the more rapidly destructive interferences make the f curve decrease for increasing values of the angle θ.

It is therefore interesting to see, using formula (61), what is the influence of variations in the behaviour of the atomic scattering factors f on the molecular scattering function. In order to simplify the problem as much as possible, Debye[44] has calculated the scattering curves for a series of imaginary diatomic molecules in which the electron atmospheres are chosen so as to facilitate the calculation of f, while the essential characteristics of actual atoms are retained. The distribution of the electrons in each atom is described by a Gaussian function. The extension of the electronic atmosphere is characterized by the length a. The electron density ρ, that is, the number of electrons in unit volume, is for each atom taken as equal to

$$\rho = \frac{1}{\pi^{\frac{3}{2}}} \frac{z}{a^3} e^{-u^2/a^2}, \tag{62}$$

u being the distance from the centre of the atom. The factor in front of the exponential is chosen so that the integral of ρ over the whole space is equal to the number z of electrons contained in the atom.

The scattering factor f for such an atom can be calculated by formula (11) of Chapter I, with the result

$$f = z\, e^{-\frac{1}{4}(k^2 s^2 a^2)}, \tag{63}$$

where $k = 2\pi/\lambda$ and $s = 2 \sin \frac{1}{2}\theta$. The scattered amplitude decreases with increasing s, that is, with increasing θ, and the decrease is the more rapid the greater the length a. In the extreme case where a is vanishingly small, all the electron atmosphere being concentrated in a point at the centre of the atom, f remains constantly equal to z. For a distance l between the two atoms in the molecule, the coherent scattering function, using formula (61), is found to be

$$\frac{\bar{I}_s}{\bar{I}_e} = 2f^2\left(1 + \frac{\sin x}{x}\right) = 2z^2 e^{-(a^2/l^2)\frac{1}{2}x^2}\left(1 + \frac{\sin x}{x}\right), \qquad (64)$$

where $x = ksl = 4\pi l(\sin\frac{1}{2}\theta)/\lambda$.

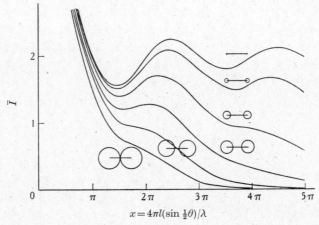

$$x = 4\pi l(\sin\tfrac{1}{2}\theta)/\lambda$$

Fig. 36. (The ordinate $\bar{I}$ is equal to $\bar{I}_s/\bar{I}_e z^2$.) (After Debye (44).)

Fig. 36 represents the scattering function calculated according to equation (64) for a series of molecules in which l is kept constant while a increases from one molecule to the next. A model of the molecule is drawn with each curve. The atoms are represented by circles of radius $a\sqrt{2}$; according to equation (62), the electron density at the circumference of these circles has fallen to $1/e^2 = 1/7\cdot39$ of its value at the centre of the atom. The curve at the top of the figure corresponds to the 'point theory' which makes $a = 0$ and $f = Z$. The following conclusions can be derived from a consideration of Fig. 36.

(a) The ratio a/l determines the general shape of the scattering function. The greater it is, the more rapidly the intensity decreases with increasing angle.

(b) As long as a/l remains small the curves show actual minima and maxima, but when a/l becomes too large these disappear and the curve becomes monotonic.

(c) The positions of the maxima are displaced more and more towards smaller angles as a/l increases. Thus, if the interatomic distance were deduced from the positions of experimental maxima by a direct comparison with the positions calculated according to the point theory, the distance l found in that way would be longer than the actual interatomic distance, the error being large for molecules in which the electron atmospheres are not very concentrated. Exact measurements therefore necessitate a comparison of the experimental curve with the *complete* theoretical curve—including incoherent scattering, the influence of which will be discussed below.

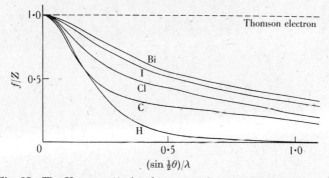

Fig. 37. The X-ray scattering factor per electron, f/Z, for the atoms H, C, Cl, I and Bi. (After Pirenne (145).)

In the case of actual molecules, the above discussion remains qualitatively valid, but the proper atomic scattering factors f must then of course be used. In order to understand the influence of the behaviour of f on the molecular scattering function, it is advisable to compare, not the f factors themselves, but rather the mean scattering factors f/Z per electron, for each kind of atom. f/Z is given in Fig. 37 for the atoms H, C, Cl, I and Bi. The heavier the atom the slower is the decrease of f/Z. The lighter atoms, the electronic atmospheres of which are more diffuse, scatter proportionately less than the heavier atoms. At values of $(\sin \frac{1}{2}\theta)/\lambda$ higher than unity, the hydrogen atom scatters practically no coherent radiation. In the case of the other atoms, however, this happens only at much higher values of this variable, on account of the high concentration of electrons in the K shell.

Experimental verifications. In order to see what remains of interatomic interferences in unfavourable cases, and in order to verify whether formula (61) and the values of the atomic scattering factors are in agreement with experimental results, Gajewski (79) has investigated the molecules N_2 and O_2, which are built up of light atoms at a short distance apart.

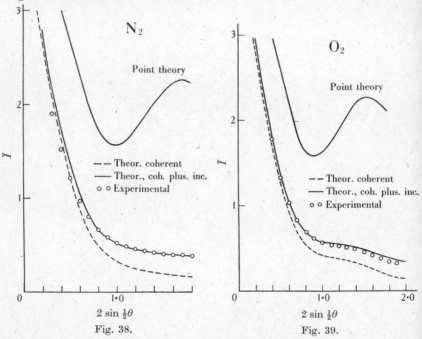

Fig. 38.   Fig. 39.

Fig. 38. X-ray scattering function for the molecule N_2. Measurements by Gajewski for $\lambda = 1\cdot54$ A. The theoretical curves are calculated for a distance $l_{N\text{-}N} = 1\cdot1$ A. (The ordinate $\bar{I}$ is equal to $\bar{I}_s/7^2I_e$.) (After Gajewski(79).)

Fig. 39. X-ray scattering function for the molecule O_2. Measurements by Gajewski for $\lambda = 1\cdot54$ A. The theoretical curves are calculated for a distance $l_{O\text{-}O} = 1\cdot2$ A. (The ordinate $\bar{I}$ is equal to $\bar{I}_s/8^2I_e$.) (After Gajewski(79).)

For nitrogen gas, using copper radiation ($\lambda = 1\cdot54$ A.), the experimental scattering curve is quite smooth, as shown in Fig. 38. So also is the curve calculated for a distance $l_{N\text{-}N} = 1\cdot1$ A. (value derived from the study of the Raman effect), using the Thomas-Fermi f values. As $Z = 7$, the Thomas-Fermi radius is

$$a = 0\cdot47/7^{\frac{1}{3}} = 0\cdot246\,\text{A.},$$

as seen in Chapter I, equation (18). Nothing remains of the

maximum which would be expected at $\theta = 120°$ according to the point theory which, making $f = Z$, assumes that the whole electron charge is concentrated at the centres of the atoms.

In the O_2 molecule, the interatomic distance is larger, $l_{O-O} = 1\cdot2$ A. and, since $Z = 8$, the radius $a = 0\cdot47/8^{\frac{1}{3}} = 0\cdot235$ A. The conditions therefore are somewhat better and the first 'maximum' accordingly is seen as a weak protuberance in the scattering curves, both observed and calculated (Fig. 39). Taking into account the incoherent intensity, the agreement of theory with experiment is satisfactory.

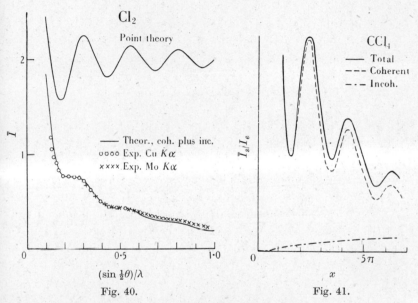

Fig. 40.   Fig. 41.

Fig. 40. X-ray scattering function for the molecule Cl_2. Measurements by Richter for $\lambda = 1\cdot54$ A. and for $\lambda = 0\cdot71$ A. The theoretical curve is calculated using the atomic factor according to Hartree. The distance $l_{Cl-Cl} = 2\cdot0$ A. (The ordinate $\bar{I}$ is equal to $\bar{I}_s/17^2I_e$.) (After Richter(152).)

Fig. 41. Theoretical X-ray scattering function for the molecule CCl_4. (The abscissa x is equal to $4\pi l (\sin \frac{1}{2}\theta)/\lambda$, l being a length characterizing the size of the molecule.) Fig. 52 shows the experimental verification of this theoretical curve. (After Bewilogua(10).)

Comparison with the point-theory curve shows how drastically the intra-atomic interferences reduce the magnitude of the intensity maximum. Although no real maximum remains, the size of the molecule has nevertheless been determined by comparing in both curves the position of other characteristic points, such as the inflexion point, and bringing the calculated value into agreement with the experimental one by a suitable choice of the length l.

It is of interest to compare with the diffraction by the O_2 molecule the diffraction by the Cl_2 molecule, in which the conditions are more favourable, for the distance $l_{Cl\text{-}Cl} = 2 \cdot 0$ A. and the Thomas-Fermi radius $a = 0 \cdot 47/17^{\frac{1}{3}} = 0 \cdot 183$ A. Fig. 40, taken from papers by Richter [151, 152], shows that the 'maxima' are more prominent than in the case of O_2, and, moreover, that they are more numerous in a given range of $(\sin \frac{1}{2}\theta)/\lambda$, because the distance l is longer. Incidentally, it may be remarked that the experimental curve is in good agreement only with the curve calculated using Hartree's factors f for chlorine. When it is compared to the curve calculated using the Thomas-Fermi factors, the discrepancies are much larger than those seen in Fig. 40. Hartree's scattering factors should therefore be used for atoms whose atomic number is lower than 18.

In the CCl_4 molecule, the most important part of the scattering is due to the group of the four Cl atoms, the mutual distances of which are equal to $2 \cdot 86$ A., being therefore larger than the Cl-Cl distance in the Cl_2 molecule. The maxima accordingly are closer together and more prominent than in Cl_2, as shown in Fig. 41. It must, however, be borne in mind that in a polyatomic molecule such as CCl_4 the periodic terms $f_i f_j (\sin x_{ij}/x_{ij})$ have a greater importance relative to the f_i^2 terms than they have in diatomic molecules, as was mentioned in Chapter I, and this in part accounts for the prominence of the CCl_4 maxima.

The examples given above show how well the predicted influence of atomic size and interatomic distance on diffraction patterns are experimentally verified.

INCOHERENT INTENSITY SCATTERED BY A MOLECULE

The incoherent intensity scattered by a molecule is equal merely to the sum of the incoherent intensities scattered by its individual atoms, and therefore constitutes a background devoid of interference effects. The incoherent intensity scattered by an atom is zero at a scattering angle $\theta = 0$, and increases with increasing values of $(\sin \tfrac{1}{2}\theta)/\lambda$, tending to a value which is proportional to the atomic number Z. As, on the other hand, the atomic scattering factors decrease with increasing angle, the intensity scattered by a molecule at very high values of $(\sin \tfrac{1}{2}\theta)/\lambda$ is predominantly incoherent and can give but little information about the structure of the molecule. The increase of the incoherent intensity function from zero to the limiting value Z is more rapid in the case of light than of heavy atoms, as has been seen in Chapter II. In the range of $(\sin \tfrac{1}{2}\theta)/\lambda$ which is useful for the determination of molecular structures, the incoherent scattering per electron therefore is more intense in the case of light than of heavy atoms.

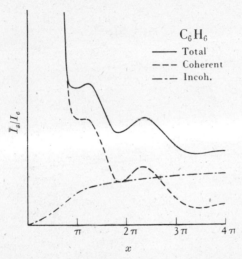

Fig. 42. Theoretical X-ray scattering function for the molecule C_6H_6. (The abscissa x is the same as in Fig. 41.) (After Bewilogua(10).)

The incoherent background has the effect of emphasizing the maxima of the coherent intensity. In the case of light atoms, the scattering factors decrease rapidly at increasing angles, but the increasing incoherent intensity is high, so that these two effects partially counterbalance each other in the resulting curve. Fig. 42 shows this for the case of C_6H_6. It is seen how large can be the relative importance of incoherent scattering in the case of molecules built up of light atoms. The figure shows that the maxima are somewhat emphasized by the effect of the incoherent background and, moreover, that the second maximum is slightly shifted towards higher angles on account of the increasing incoherent background. Similar effects occur in the case of the CCl_4 molecule, but are less important because the incoherent scattering is relatively much less intense in this case, as shown in Fig. 41.

X-RAY DIFFRACTION FORMULA

For a free molecule, built up of the atoms $1, 2, \ldots, i, \ldots, j, \ldots, n$, all of which can be considered as having a spherically symmetrical atmosphere, and which are situated at constant distances l_{ij} from one another, it follows from the above considerations that the mean intensity $\bar{I}_s$ scattered at any angle θ between primary and secondary ray is given by the following formula, in the case of unpolarized primary radiation:

$$\bar{I}_s = \frac{I_0}{R^2} \frac{1 + \cos^2 \theta}{2} a_e^2 \left[\underbrace{\sum_i \sum_j f_i f_j \frac{\sin x_{ij}}{x_{ij}}}_{\text{coherent}} + \underbrace{Q \sum_i Z_i S_i}_{\text{incoherent}} \right]. \tag{65}$$

The meaning of the letters is as follows: I_0 is the primary intensity, R is the distance from the molecule to the observation point, $a_e = 2 \cdot 81 \times 10^{-13}$ cm. is the classical radius of the electron, f_i is the atomic scattering factor of atom i, $x_{ij} = 4\pi l_{ij}(\sin \frac{1}{2}\theta)/\lambda$, λ is the wave-length, Z_i is the atomic number of atom i, S_i is the incoherent scattering function per electron for atom i, and Q is the relativistic correction for incoherent scattering, given in Chapter II and rewritten here:

$$Q = \frac{1}{\left(1 + \dfrac{h(1 - \cos \theta)}{mc\lambda}\right)^3}, \tag{66}$$

where h is Planck's constant, m the mass of the electron, and c the velocity of light. It must be pointed out that the above formula does not take into account the continual variations in the distances l_{ij} which are brought about by thermal movements inside the molecule, the influence of which is discussed in Chapter VIII.

As a concrete example, equation (65) may be developed for the case of the CCl_4 molecule. The molecule is taken to be a regular tetrahedron with the C atom at the centre, so that all Cl-Cl distances are equal, as are all C-Cl distances. The following table may be written out in order to find all the terms x_{ij} of the sum $\sum_i \sum_j$ of the coherent intensity:

	C	Cl_1	Cl_2	Cl_3	Cl_4
C	0	C-Cl	C-Cl	C-Cl	C-Cl
Cl_1	C-Cl	0	Cl-Cl	Cl-Cl	Cl-Cl
Cl_2	C-Cl	Cl-Cl	0	Cl-Cl	Cl-Cl
Cl_3	C-Cl	Cl-Cl	Cl-Cl	0	Cl-Cl
Cl_4	C-Cl	Cl-Cl	Cl-Cl	Cl-Cl	0

It shows that there are twelve periodic terms in $x_{Cl\text{-}Cl}$, eight periodic terms in $x_{C\text{-}Cl}$, one monotonic term f_C^2 and four monotonic terms f_{Cl}^2. The incoherent intensity scattered by the molecule is given by the sum of the incoherent intensity scattered by the four Cl atoms $(4Z_{Cl} \times S_{Cl})$ and by the C atom $(Z_C \times S_C)$, the functions S being obtained using Table II, as explained in Chapter II.

Suppose a small volume of carbon tetrachloride vapour is irradiated by a beam of unpolarized X-rays. This volume contains N molecules, N being of the order of 10^{16} for a volume of 1 mm.^{3} Then the scattered intensity $\bar{I}_s$ is, neglecting the intermolecular interferences, which will be discussed in the next chapter,

$$\bar{I}_s = N \frac{I_0}{R^2} \frac{1 + \cos^2\theta}{2} a_e^2 \left[\underbrace{4f_{Cl}^2 + f_C^2 + 12f_{Cl}^2 \frac{\sin\left(4\pi l_{Cl\text{-}Cl}\dfrac{\sin\frac{1}{2}\theta}{\lambda}\right)}{4\pi l_{Cl\text{-}Cl}\dfrac{\sin\frac{1}{2}\theta}{\lambda}}}_{\text{coherent}} \right.$$

$$\left. + \underbrace{8f_{Cl}f_C \frac{\sin\left(4\pi l_{C\text{-}Cl}\dfrac{\sin\frac{1}{2}\theta}{\lambda}\right)}{4\pi l_{C\text{-}Cl}\dfrac{\sin\frac{1}{2}\theta}{\lambda}}}_{\text{coherent}} + \underbrace{\frac{4 \times 17 S_{Cl} + 6 S_C}{\left(1 + \dfrac{h(1 - \cos\theta)}{mc\lambda}\right)^3}}_{\text{incoherent}} \right]; \quad (67)$$

f and S are generally functions of the variable $(\sin\frac{1}{2}\theta)/\lambda$ only, but the relativity correction Q for the incoherent scattering depends directly upon θ. In some cases where the incoherent scattering is not intense, as for CCl_4, this correction may be neglected, when the whole expression between brackets becomes a function of $(\sin\frac{1}{2}\theta)/\lambda$. Such a function is represented, for example, by Fig. 41.

CHAPTER VII

INTERMOLECULAR INTERFERENCES IN GASES AND LIQUIDS. 'OUTER EFFECT'

GENERAL

THE preceding chapters study the interference effects which occur inside a single atom or a single molecule. In experimental practice, large numbers of atoms or molecules are always dealt with at a time. It is therefore necessary to discuss the additional interferences which occur between any molecule and all its neighbours. Whereas, in X-ray diffraction by gases, this 'outer effect' is in most cases of negligible importance, in diffraction by liquids it is as important as the 'inner effect'—that is, the interferences arising inside each single molecule—and in some cases it may yield information about the arrangement of the molecules in the liquid. In molecular crystals, the 'outer effect' of course is very important because of the regular distribution and orientation of the molecules, but, for this very reason, the structure of the individual molecules building up the crystal may be determined from measurements of the X-ray reflexion intensities. The case of gases and liquids only will be considered here.

In the first investigations which were made on the diffraction of X-rays by liquids, it was thought that the properties of the scattering function depended only upon the shape and dimensions of the individual molecules. Meanwhile, however, it became evident that very large numbers of different liquids yield diffraction patterns which show only slight differences from one another. This led to the idea that the inner, and most intense, diffraction ring must be due to interferences arising between secondary waves which originate from different molecules of the liquid (38). The experiments of Keesom and de Smedt (114), who, in particular, observed an interference ring in the diffraction of X-rays by liquid argon, a monatomic liquid, were conclusive in proving the existence of this important 'outer effect'. An historical account of the investigation of the structure of liquids has been given by Debye and Menke (46).

'OUTER EFFECT' IN GASES

The exact theory of the outer effect appears to be as difficult as the theory of the correction for the dimensions of the molecules in the equation of state. Nevertheless, a first approximation can readily be obtained for the limiting case in which the total volume occupied by the molecules is small compared with the volume occupied by the gas. In this case, Debye (37, 38) has shown that, if the molecules are comparable with hard spheres and interact only by preventing each other from entering into the domains defined by these spheres, this alone is sufficient to cause the scattering function to exhibit a maximum. This maximum occurs at an angle determined by the ratio of the wave-length to the diameter of the hypothetical spheres.

The theoretical problem can be attacked in the following way. A beam of unpolarized primary X-rays, of wave-length λ and of amplitude equal to unity, strikes a large number, N, of particles occupying at a given moment certain positions in space. Each of these particles is spherically symmetrical and gives rise in all directions to scattered radiation having an amplitude and phase defined in the usual way by a scattering factor f. Such a system resembles a monatomic gas. The intensity scattered at a given moment by the system of particles can be calculated. In fact, however, this intensity cannot be observed when the particles are in motion, as are the molecules of a gas. All that can be measured is the mean value of the intensity scattered during an appreciable time, large in comparison with the time necessary for the particles to become thoroughly interchanged in position, and it is this mean intensity which must be calculated. This case, of course, is different from that of the rigid atomic framework of a molecule taking all possible orientations in space, for here no constant structure at all is retained during the course of time; on the contrary, the particles take up at random all positions in space.

The gas is considered to be not very dense, so that, when dealing with two particles m and n, the other particles need not be taken into account, and, moreover, it is unnecessary to distinguish between the real volume of the gas and the free volume in which the molecules can move. In order to calculate the mean scattered intensity, it is necessary to know the probability that a particle m has its centre in the element dV_m of the total volume V, while a second particle n simultaneously has its centre in the element dV_n situated at a distance r_{mn} from dV_m. This probability can be written

$$W \frac{dV_m}{V} \frac{dV_n}{V}. \tag{68}$$

If all relative positions were equally probable, W would everywhere be equal to unity. The particles are considered to be impenetrable spheres of radius a. Thus $2a$ is the radius of the 'sphere of action' of each particle, which is the domain inside which the centre of another particle cannot be found. This imposes upon the probability function W the condition that it must be zero for distances r_{mn} smaller than $2a$, while it is equal to unity for

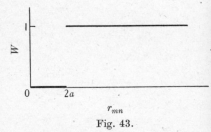

Fig. 43.

distances r_{mn} larger than $2a$ (Fig. 43). Under these conditions the calculations of Debye (38) give for the mean intensity $\bar{I}_s$ scattered by the gas the expression

$$\bar{I}_s = N \frac{1 + \cos^2 \theta}{2} \frac{a_e^2}{R^2} f^2 \left[1 - \frac{\Omega}{V} \phi(2ksa) \right]. \tag{69}$$

The term in Ω/V represents the outer effect; Ω is the total volume of the spheres of action of all the particles:

$$\Omega = N \frac{4\pi}{3} (2a)^3. \tag{70}$$

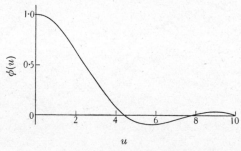

Fig. 44. (After Debye (38).)

$\phi(u)$ is the following function:

$$\phi(u) = \frac{3}{u^3}(\sin u - u \cos u) \tag{71}$$

and

$$2ksa = 8\pi a \frac{\sin \frac{1}{2}\theta}{\lambda}, \tag{72}$$

remembering that $k = 2\pi/\lambda$. In Fig. 44 the function $\phi(u)$, equation (71), is plotted against u. For $u = 0$ it is found that $\phi = 1$; as the value of the argument increases, the function ϕ eventually becomes zero, and then performs oscillations of decreasing amplitude.

Each particle may be supposed to scatter X-rays in the same way as a Thomson electron, in which case f is equal to unity. The radius a may be chosen so that $2a/\lambda = 3$, the spheres having, for instance, a diameter $2a = 2\cdot1$ A. and the wave-length being $\lambda = 0\cdot7$ A. The factor Ω/V may be put equal to $\frac{1}{2}$. Under these con-

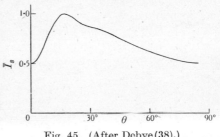

Fig. 45. (After Debye (38).)

ditions the scattering function is, neglecting the factor $N(a^2/R^2)$,

$$\bar{I}_s = \frac{1 + \cos^2\theta}{2}[1 - \tfrac{1}{2}\phi(12\pi \sin \tfrac{1}{2}\theta)]. \tag{73}$$

It is reproduced in Fig. 45, which shows that a ring having a maximum of intensity would be observed at an angle θ of about 16°.

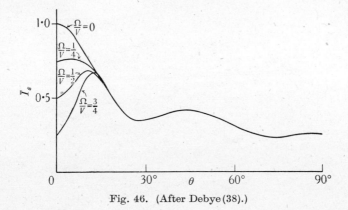

Fig. 46. (After Debye (38).)

Formerly it had been claimed by some that the presence of an interference ring must be connected with the existence of double molecules, on the grounds that no other cause seemed to be available for explaining such an interference effect. The above calculations prove that this view is entirely wrong, for it has been supposed in them that the particles behave as hard spheres and do not show any association, and yet the theory shows that a strong interference ring would be observed under these conditions.

It is also interesting to calculate the scattering function for the simplified model of a diatomic gas. Let N spherical impenetrable particles of radius a be considered, each containing now, instead of one, two spherically symmetrical scattering centres separated by a distance l. The line connecting these scattering centres passes through the centre of the particle, which is therefore at an equal distance $\frac{1}{2}l$ from each of them. With such a system, the interferences which take place between two molecules depend not only upon the length and orientation of the straight line joining the molecular centres, but also upon the orientation of the molecules themselves relative to the primary ray. The molecular scattering factors are not independent of the orientations of the molecules relative to the incident beam, as are the atomic factors. This fact introduces an additional complication in the calculations. These give (38) the following result for the value of the mean scattered intensity:

$$\bar{I}_s = 4N\frac{1+\cos^2\theta}{2}\frac{a_e^2}{R^2}f^2\left\{\frac{1}{2}\left[1+\frac{\sin ksl}{ksl}\right]-\frac{\Omega}{V}\left[\frac{\sin\frac{1}{2}ksl}{\frac{1}{2}ksl}\right]^2\phi(2ksa)\right\}; \quad (74)$$

f is the scattering factor of each diffracting centre, ϕ the function defined by equation (71) and given in Fig. 44. Here again the term in Ω/V represents the outer effect.

With decreasing gas density the importance of the second term in equation (74) decreases. At very low densities the 'outer effect' vanishes, and the 'inner effect' alone remains. The scattering function then assumes the limiting form

$$\bar{I}_s = N\frac{1+\cos^2\theta}{2}\frac{a_e^2}{R^2}2f^2\left[1+\frac{\sin ksl}{ksl}\right], \quad (75)$$

which can be deduced from equation (61) of the preceding chapter simply by multiplying the intensity scattered by one isolated molecule by the total number, N, of molecules.

Equation (74) has been calculated taking $2a/\lambda = 3$ and $l = a$. This may, for example, be considered to correspond to a wavelength $\lambda = 0 \cdot 7$ A., a particle diameter of $2 \cdot 1$ A. and a distance $1 \cdot 05$ A. between the scattering centres. The scattering factor f is again taken equal to unity. The shape of the scattering function depends upon the density of the gas, which is given by the quotient Ω/V. Four curves are drawn in Fig. 46, corresponding respectively to the values 0, $\frac{1}{4}$, $\frac{1}{2}$ and $\frac{3}{4}$ for this quotient (the factor $4Na_e^2/R^2$ is disregarded). The figure shows how the first maximum which, at high gas densities, occurs at an angle θ of about $12°$ and which is due to intermolecular interferences, disappears at low densities. A second maximum, which occurs at $\theta = 45°$ and which is due to the interference between the two centres contained in each particle, remains unaffected by the variations of density.

In the diffraction of X-rays by real gases, the scattering curve must also show a superposition of the inner and outer effects. Now the importance of the outer effect must be expected always to be proportional to the gas density, as it is in the special cases represented by equations (69) and (74). By making a series of measurements under decreasing gas pressures, therefore, it must always be possible to arrive at a determination of the inner effect alone, eliminating the outer effect by extrapolating to zero pressure.

In most experiments made in order to determine molecular structures, the pressure of the gas is of the order of 1 atm. and the ratio Ω/V is of the order of only 10^{-3}, so that the outer effect may simply be neglected, especially when measurements are not made at very small values of the angle θ.

In agreement with this, Herzog[97] observed no pressure effect while working with argon under $2 \cdot 5$ atm.[†], but Harvey[93], using nitrogen gas under 60, 80 and 100 atm., found at these high pressures a marked decrease of the intensity towards smaller scattering angles, as predicted by the theory.

It must be emphasized that the validity of formulae (69) and (74) depends entirely on the assumptions which have been made about

[†] Not 26 atm., see erratum in [98].

the probability function W which is represented by Fig. 43. These particular assumptions are a fair approximation in the case of ordinary gases, but the conditions are quite different in liquids.

X-RAY DIFFRACTION BY MONATOMIC LIQUIDS

Theory. It is found experimentally that a monatomic liquid like mercury gives very strong X-ray interferences, as shown in Fig. 47. Actually, the interferences are much stronger than would be expected according to a formula of type (69), even allowing for the fact that this equation is strictly valid only for low densities. The effect observed must be explained by a certain regularity in the arrangement of the atoms in the liquid, and the mean distribution of the atoms in liquid mercury, that is, the probability function W of formula (68) may be derived from the experimental scattering curve.

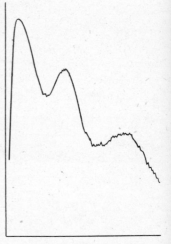

It is known from its thermodynamic properties that liquid mercury is nearly a perfect liquid. This being the case, it can be assumed that mercury atoms act in the same way in all directions in space. If we consider two volume elements dV_1 and dV_2 at a distance r

Fig. 47. Tracing of a microphotometer record of the diffraction of X-rays by liquid mercury. (After Debye and Menke(46).)

apart in the total volume V, and two atoms 1 and 2, the probability of finding atom 1 in dV_1 and, at the same time, atom 2 in dV_2 can then be represented by

$$W(r)\frac{dV_1}{V}\frac{dV_2}{V}, \tag{76}$$

where W is a function of the distance r only. For large distances r, it is to be expected that $W = 1$, since all mutual positions are then equally probable, and, for very short distances, $W = 0$, since the atoms cannot interpenetrate each other. The problem is to determine $W(r)$ in the intermediate region.

Debye and Menke [46] first calculate as a function of $W(r)$ the mean intensity $\bar{I}_s$ scattered by the liquid, finding

$$\bar{I}_s = N\frac{1+\cos^2\theta}{2}f^2\left[1-\frac{4\pi}{d^3}\int_0^\infty (1-W)\frac{\sin ksr}{ksr}r^2 dr\right], \quad (77)$$

where $d^3 = V/N$, N being the total number of atoms, so that d^3 represents the volume at the disposal of each atom in the liquid; the coefficient $I_0 a_e^2/R^2$ is omitted in the formula.

If the dimensionless variable $\rho = r/\lambda$ is introduced, equation (77) can be written

$$\bar{I}_s = N\frac{1+\cos^2\theta}{2}f^2\left[1-\frac{\lambda^3}{d^3}\frac{2}{s}\int_0^\infty (1-W)\sin(2\pi\rho s)\rho d\rho\right]. \quad (78)$$

If the function $W(r)$ were known, the angular distribution of the mean scattered intensity could be calculated using equation (77) or (78). Conversely, it can be supposed that the scattering function has been measured experimentally, that is, that $\bar{I}_s$ is known as a function of θ, or of s. It can be written

$$\bar{I}_s = N\frac{1+\cos^2\theta}{2}f^2 E(s). \quad (79)$$

Since f^2, which represents the scattering by an isolated atom, is known, the expression E can then be considered as experimentally known. From a comparison of equations (78) and (79) it follows that

$$s(1-E) = 2\frac{\lambda^3}{d^3}\int_0^\infty \rho(1-W)\sin(2\pi\rho s)\,d\rho. \quad (80)$$

Now Fourier's theorem may be expressed in the following way: if

$$f(x) = 2\int_0^\infty \phi(\xi)\sin(2\pi\xi x)\,d\xi, \quad (81)$$

then

$$\phi(\xi) = 2\int_0^\infty f(x)\sin(2\pi\xi x)\,dx. \quad (82)$$

This transformation can immediately be applied to equation (80) in order to determine $W(\rho)$, knowing $E(s)$. The following result is obtained [46]:

$$\rho(1-W) = 2\frac{d^3}{\lambda^3}\int_0^\infty s(1-E)\sin(2\pi\rho s)\,ds. \quad (83)$$

This relation, which was given first by Zernike and Prins [182] in a somewhat different form, forms the basis of the determination of the distribution function $W(r)$ for liquid mercury.

Experiments on liquid mercury. The quantitative study of the diffraction of X-rays by liquid mercury and the experimental determination of the probability function W have been made by Menke (126).

In order to be able to derive definite conclusions about the structure of liquids, accurate measurements of the scattered intensity are indispensable. For using the Fourier analysis outlined above, it is quite insufficient merely to establish that interference maxima occur at some definite angles. A continuous curve of exact intensities

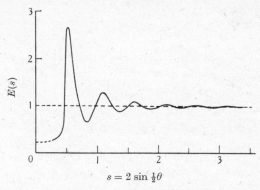

Fig. 48. Experimental function $E(s)$ for liquid mercury.

(The curve is drawn for copper radiation of wave-length 1·54 A. The results obtained using molybdenum radiation, of wave-length 0·71 A., have been re-calculated so as to fit the copper radiation curve, keeping the same abscissa s, and the curve is accordingly prolonged farther than $s = 2$.) (After Menke (126).)

covering as large an angular range as possible is absolutely necessary as a basis for such an analysis.[†] Menke's experimental procedure, consisting of measuring the diffraction from the free surface of the liquid, was chosen in such a way as to obtain the final result with as few corrections for secondary effects as possible. The chief of these is absorption, the influence of which can in this case be

---

[†] For instance, Zernike and Prins (182) remark that they themselves were unable to use formula (83) on account of the lack of such quantitative data.

It is hardly necessary to point out that, according to the above mathematical developments, there exists no direct and simple relationship between the position of the maxima in the intensity curve and that of the maxima in the distribution curve W.

accurately estimated. The theory given above evidently refers only to coherent scattering; the incoherent intensity is therefore calculated and subtracted from the experimental scattering function. Then the function $E(s)$ is calculated according to equation (79), knowing the atomic scattering factor f for mercury. $E(s)$ is represented by Fig. 48. Next, the integral of equation (83) is calculated for every value of $\rho = r/\lambda$ in order to obtain the function $\rho(1 - W)$. Hence the probability function W is obtained. It is represented in Fig. 49 as a function of r. The meaning of this function is as follows.

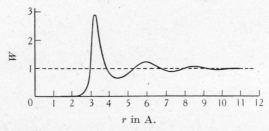

Fig. 49. Probability function $W(r)$ for liquid mercury. (After Menke (126).)

Let us observe in liquid mercury two atoms, arbitrarily chosen. Around one of these atoms, at a distance r, we imagine a shell-shaped volume element dV, limited by two spheres having as centre the centre of the atom, and accompanying the atom in all its displacements. The ordinate W, corresponding to the abscissa r in Fig. 49, then gives the mean length of time during which the centre of the second atom will be found inside the volume element dV.

For distances r shorter than about 2 A., the function W is equal to zero:[†] no mercury atom centre can come closer to the centre of another atom than this distance, because the atoms cannot interpenetrate. At slightly longer distances, W rises sharply, and presents a prominent maximum at $r = 3 \cdot 3$ A.: the atoms therefore are often situated such a distance apart. Subsequently, W presents a minimum at $r = 4 \cdot 4$ A.: this value therefore corresponds but rarely to the mutual distance of the atoms. There is another maximum of W, less prominent than the first, at $r = 6$ A., which is

---

† The results have verified this down to $r = 1 \cdot 5$ A. At smaller values of r the curve oscillates again, due to the fact that the higher order intensity maxima, which mainly determine this part of the W curve, are not known sufficiently accurately. The curve therefore is not drawn for values of r smaller than $1 \cdot 5$ A.

therefore a favoured mutual distance, and a shallow minimum at $r = 7 \cdot 3$ A., a distance which tends to be avoided. A third very weak maximum of W exists at $r = 8 \cdot 5$ A. At larger values of r the oscillations of the function W become very small. All mutual distances above 10 A. occur with almost equal probabilities.

This structure of liquid mercury is the cause of the strong intensity maxima obtained in the diffraction of X-rays by this substance. This is seen by referring to the theoretical scattering function reproduced in Fig. 45, which corresponds to the simple probability distribution given in Fig. 43. Compared to those given by liquid mercury, the interference effects shown in this scattering curve are quite weak.

In the case of a crystal, the arrangement of the atoms remains perfectly regular throughout the lattice. The predominance of certain distances is therefore complete; there are no intermediate interatomic distances. The probability function W of Fig. 49 expresses quantitatively to what extent the structure characteristic of the crystal, which the motion of the atoms in the liquid must tend to destroy, is actually retained in liquid mercury. The cause of this *quasi-crystalline* structure of the liquid is essentially the space requirement of each of the atoms: from models made of steel balls, distribution functions which are analogous to the above function for mercury have been experimentally deduced [126].

These experiments on the diffraction of X-rays by liquid mercury thus prove that, *in domains extending over a few atomic diameters, there is a regularity in the spatial arrangement of the atoms in the liquid which is similar to that which exists in crystals.*[†]

X-RAY DIFFRACTION BY POLYATOMIC LIQUIDS

Using the same technique as for liquid mercury, Menke [126] has obtained for liquid carbon tetrachloride, CCl_4, the experimental scattering function represented by the broken line in Fig. 50.[‡]

A comparison of this function with that for the free CCl_4 molecule, shown in Fig. 63 of p. 103, immediately reveals important

---

[†] A recent review of the diffraction of X-rays by liquid elements has been made by Gingrich [81]. Results somewhat different from Menke's are given in a recent paper by Campbell and Hildebrand [23] on mercury.

[‡] For more recent measurements on liquid CCl_4, see [19] and [70].

differences at the smaller scattering angles. The first maximum for
the liquid appears at an angle substantially smaller than the first
maximum for the gas. This corresponds to the fact that in the liquid
the distances between molecule and molecule give rise to the first
maximum, and these distances are larger than the distances between the atoms inside each molecule which are responsible for the
maxima of the gas curve. Towards the smallest angles the intensity
decreases sharply in the case of the liquid, while it increases for the
gas. This is a generally observed phenomenon which is explained
by the above considerations regarding the outer effect.

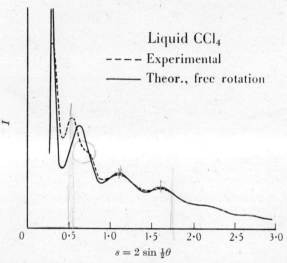

Fig. 50. X-ray scattering curves for liquid carbon tetrachloride, measured, and
calculated assuming free rotation of the molecules CCl_4 in the liquid. The discrepancies between the two curves prove that the rotation of the molecules in the
liquid is hindered. (Concerning the abscissa s, see the note under Fig. 48.) (After
Menke (126).)

From the fourth maximum of the liquid curve (found at about
$s = 1 \cdot 1$), which corresponds to the second maximum for the gas, the
two curves agree fairly well with one another—and with the
theoretical curve for free rotation in the liquid, discussed below.
This is due to the fact that, at these angles, the outer effect
practically disappears and the inner effect alone remains (43, 146).
*At large angles, therefore, the molecules in the liquid scatter nearly as
if they were isolated and free.*

Menke has calculated the scattering function which would correspond to liquid CCl_4 if the two following assumptions were true:

(a) The molecules in the liquid can rotate freely.

(b) The centres of the molecules are distributed in space according to a probability law similar to that found for the atoms of liquid mercury.

Fig. 50 shows the theoretical curve which is obtained under these conditions. Now this curve is in definite disagreement with the observed curve at small scattering angles, where the outer effect is important. This proves that the above conditions (a) and (b) are not fulfilled in the actual CCl_4 liquid. A closer discussion leads to the conclusion that it is assumption (a) which is incorrect. At short ranges, therefore, *all relative orientations of the molecules in the liquid are not equally probable*. The CCl_4 molecules do not rotate freely. They do not behave like spheres, although their symmetrical structure might have suggested this as a possibility.

No Fourier analysis of the X-ray data on liquid CCl_4 has been made by Menke, because formula (83), giving the distribution probability W, is valid for the case of monatomic liquids only. In the case of polyatomic liquids, molecular scattering factors must be used in the calculations in place of the atomic scattering factors f. Since these molecular factors depend upon the orientation of the molecules relative to the primary ray, as well as upon the scattering angle θ, their product cannot be brought out as a factor, as has been done with the f^2 products of formula (77). On the contrary, their variability must be taken into account in the integration giving the mean scattered intensity. The formulae obtained in this way are of a form such that the Fourier transformation cannot be applied to them.

It is important to remark that the properties of the scattering curve depend both on the probability W and on the probability of orientation of the molecules. In principle, it is therefore impossible to determine *both* probability functions using only the data of the scattering curve which is a function of one variable only, namely, the scattering angle. One of the probability functions must be known from another source. Simple *a priori* assumptions about the probability of orientation of the molecules are not legitimate, however, as has been seen for the assumption of completely free rotation in liquid CCl_4. It follows that the arrangement of the molecules in a liquid cannot in general be uniquely determined from X-ray diffraction experiments alone. And it is evident that X-ray diffraction by liquids is not well suited for determining the structure of molecules.

What can in all cases be derived uniquely from the diffraction pattern of a liquid, according to Debye[54], is the temporal mean $\overline{\delta_1 \delta_2}$ of the product $\delta_1 \delta_2$, in which δ_1 and δ_2 are the fluctuations of electron density occurring, on account of thermal motion, in the volume elements dV_1 and dV_2, fixed in space and situated a distance r apart. On account of the isotropy of the liquid, $\overline{\delta_1 \delta_2}$ is evidently a function of the distance r only. (If δ_1 and δ_2 are completely independent of one another, $\overline{\delta_1 \delta_2}$ is equal to zero.) This function $\overline{\delta_1 \delta_2}$ can in all cases be derived uniquely from the angular distribution of the coherent intensity, using the kind of Fourier reversal introduced by Zernike and Prins. As has been seen, however, it is not generally possible, without arbitrary assumptions, to go further and to determine the positions and orientations of the molecules, whose translations and rotations in the liquid are the cause of the density fluctuations δ.

CHAPTER VIII

THERMAL MOVEMENTS IN MOLECULES

I. VIBRATIONS

General and experimental. In the preceding chapters, scattering functions have been calculated assuming that the molecules are rigid atomic frameworks. In actual molecules, however, each atom oscillates about its equilibrium position on account of temperature vibrations and zero-point energy. The scattering functions must be corrected in order to take this effect into account. In the first experiments on CCl_4 gas [40,9], although the general agreement of the measurements with the rigid framework theory was satisfactory, nevertheless the ratio of the intensity of the maxima to that of the minima, especially at large angles, was smaller than was predicted by the theory. It is precisely an effect of this kind that would be expected to arise from the atomic vibrations. It was therefore necessary to see if the amplitudes of the movements inside the molecule were of such a magnitude as would quantitatively explain the observed effect. This question was investigated theoretically by James [110] who concluded that the temperature effect is quite slight if one does not go to high values of $(\sin \frac{1}{2}\theta)/\lambda$. The explanation of the discrepancies referred to above, therefore, had to be sought, not in the thermal movements, but in the fact that the X-ray radiation used in the early experiments was not strictly monochromatic [86].

In order to prove the existence of such a temperature effect, it would obviously be best to demonstrate experimentally that differences exist between the diffraction curves obtained at two different temperatures for a given molecule. The temperature effect could then be calculated from known molecular constants and compared with observation.

The calculations are easiest for diatomic molecules such as Cl_2 and O_2, but the amplitude of the vibrations is small in these molecules, and they give no prominent maxima in their diffraction curves. Tetrahedral molecules such as CCl_4 or $SiCl_4$, on the contrary, give very prominent maxima, and the amplitude of the atomic motions is greater in them, while the geometrical conditions remain simple enough to allow a theoretical treatment of the problem. Infra-red and Raman spectra show that the amplitudes are larger in $SiCl_4$ than in CCl_4, and James (110) accordingly chose the $SiCl_4$ molecule for study. A diffraction photograph was taken at 100° C., another at 300° C. and another again at 100° C., without making any change in the apparatus. The photographs give the first three maxima and cover a $(\sin \frac{1}{2}\theta)/\lambda$ range extending from 0·1 to 0·6 (λ in A.). The differences between the curves obtained at 100 and 300° C. lie within the limits of error (except for an insignificant difference at the first maximum). The temperature effect thus appears to be too small to be measured. Similarly, van der Grinten (86), using strictly monochromatic X-rays and an improved experimental arrangement, obtained at temperatures of 100 and 320° C. diffraction photographs of CCl_4 which could not be distinguished from one another.

This agrees with the theory. Fig. 51 shows the scattering function calculated by James for $SiCl_4$, (a) using a rigid model, according to equation (65), and (b) taking into account the vibrations in the molecules at 300° C. The differences between these two curves are small. The differences between the curves giving the temperature effect at 300 and 100° C. are so much smaller still that they cannot be shown on the figure, so that the above experimental results are quite understandable.

The temperature interval 100–300° C. thus being too small to produce appreciable differences in the diffraction curves, it remained necessary to compare the absolute shape of an experimental with that of the corresponding theoretical curve, in order perhaps to bring to light the influence of zero-point energy and thermal vibrations. Here accurate intensity measurements are necessary. Such measurements have been made by van der Grinten for CCl_4 (86). Fig. 51 shows how slight is the temperature effect to be expected, however, and in fact van der Grinten's observed curve, which is reproduced in Fig. 52, agrees satisfactorily with the theoretical curve even without temperature correction. The differences between the two curves lie within the experimental error. The effect of

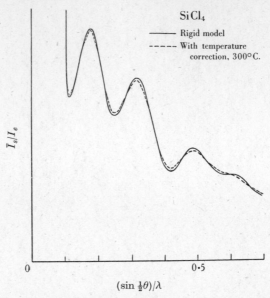

Fig. 51. Theoretical X-ray scattering function for the molecule $SiCl_4$ calculated first for a rigid model, and secondly taking into account zero-point energy and thermal vibrations at 300° C. (After James (110).)

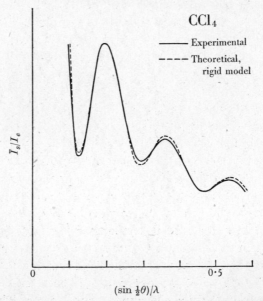

Fig. 52. X-ray scattering function for the molecule CCl_4, measured using crystal-reflected $Cu K\alpha$ radiation, and calculated without temperature correction. (After van der Grinten (86).)

vibrations and zero-point energy in the molecule thus cannot be shown experimentally in the range of $(\sin \frac{1}{2}\theta)/\lambda$ which has been investigated in X-ray diffraction.

As the calculation of the temperature correction is very troublesome, it is interesting to know that in cases such as the above the correction is not large. But the theory points out that its importance increases rapidly with increasing values of $(\sin \frac{1}{2}\theta)/\lambda$, and the X-ray investigations have been made only at small values of $(\sin \frac{1}{2}\theta)/\lambda$, that is, in the region where the most prominent intensity maxima are to be found. In electron diffraction by gases, however, the outer 'maxima' of the diffraction pattern are not unimportant, while the temperature effect is fundamentally the same as in X-ray diffraction. It was actually shown [58,59] in an investigation of CCl_4 by electron diffraction that the temperature correction is necessary at the fifth apparent maximum in order to obtain agreement between calculation and observation.

As the complete account of this investigation made by Degard and van der Grinten has not been published in a readily available periodical, it may be useful to give some details here. Smooth microphotometer records of the diffraction photographs were obtained by rotating the plate around the centre of the diffraction rings. These records are not directly comparable to the theoretical intensity curves because they depend upon the law of blackening of the plate and upon the sensitivity of the microphotometer. In order to solve this difficulty, monotonic curves, without the periodic intensity terms, were drawn through the experimental records. Correspondence was then assumed to exist between the theoretical monotonic curve and this experimental curve: this provided an experimental intensity scale. The complete experimental intensity curve could be derived using this scale, but in fact the following procedure was employed. Tangents to the two curves were drawn at the intersection of the monotonic curve with the complete curve, these making respectively with the abscissa the angles α and β. Now, from the correspondence assumed above, it follows that the ratio $\tan \alpha / \tan \beta$ must be the same for the microphotometer record and the theoretical intensity curve. Basing the calculations on a rigid model, it was impossible to obtain such an agreement at the fifth maximum, even when wide changes were made in the experimental conditions. The curve is more inclined in A than is predicted by the theory (Fig. 53). The monochromatism of the electron beam was controlled. It was also verified that no decreasing parasitic background existed on the photograph and a tube was built to absorb the primary beam shortly after the diffraction, but the disagreement persisted. Then the calculations of James were applied and gave the point curve of Fig. 53, which corresponds better with the

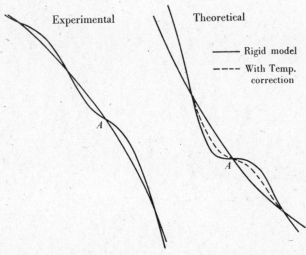

Fig. 53. The fifth apparent maximum of the electron diffraction curve for the molecule CCl_4, experimental and theoretical. The theoretical curve has been calculated, first for a rigid model and, secondly, using James's temperature correction. (After Degard and van der Grinten(59).)

measured curve. Further verification was obtained by a study of the first maximum, for which the temperature correction is negligible. Fig. 54 shows that measured and calculated curves there are in agreement.

Theoretical. The problem of the scattering of radiation by a free molecule built of oscillating atoms has been treated classically by James(110).[†] The scattering function is the mean of the intensity scattered by the molecule, this mean being taken (a) for all possible positions of the atoms in the molecule, and (b) for all orientations

† See also Debye(55).

of the molecule in space. In the same way as the classical treatment of the scattering by one-electron atoms gives the total scattering, coherent plus incoherent, of this atom, James's calculations must give the sum of the coherent intensity scattered by the molecule, plus the incoherent intensity which is due to intramolecular vibrations. The incoherent scattering of the atoms themselves must be added separately.

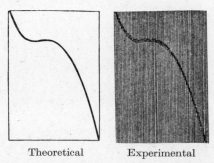

Theoretical   Experimental

Fig. 54. The first maximum of the electron diffraction curve for the molecule CCl_4, experimental and theoretical. (After Degard and van der Grinten(59).)

In the range of $(\sin \frac{1}{2}\theta)/\lambda$ which has been investigated, the result may be written, as a good approximation,

$$\bar{I}_s = \frac{I_0}{R^2} \frac{1 + \cos^2 \theta}{2} a_e^2 \left[\sum_i \sum_j e^{-A_{ij}} f_i f_j \frac{\sin x_{ij}}{x_{ij}} + Q \sum_i Z_i S_i \right]. \quad (84)$$

The symbols have the same meaning as in formula (65) which has been obtained for the case of a rigid molecule, but l_{ij} here represents the distance between the equilibrium positions of the atoms i and j, and the exponent $-A_{ij}$ of the new exponential factor is given by

$$A_{ij} = 8\pi^2 \left(\frac{\sin \frac{1}{2}\theta}{\lambda}\right)^2 \overline{\delta l_{ij}^2}, \quad (85)$$

$\overline{\delta l_{ij}^2}$ being the mean square variation of the distance between atoms i and j. This formula differs from the rigid frame formula (65) only by the introduction of the factors e^{-A}: it becomes identical with it for $\overline{\delta l^2} = 0$, which makes $e^{-A} = 1$. It must be noted that the corrections e^{-A} apply only to the periodic intensity terms of the double sum, that is, to those for which $i \neq j$. For, when $i = j$, $l_{ii} = 0$, and $\overline{\delta l_{ii}^2}$ is evidently zero. In particular, it may be worth pointing out that, in the case of monatomic gases, the double sum reduces to f^2 and there is no temperature or zero-point energy correction.

In the simple case of the Cl_2 molecule, for instance, the double sum $\sum_i \sum_j$ of formula (84) is written

$$2f_{Cl}^2 \left[1 + e^{-A} \frac{\sin\left(4\pi l\dfrac{\sin\frac{1}{2}\theta}{\lambda}\right)}{4\pi l\dfrac{\sin\frac{1}{2}\theta}{\lambda}} \right], \tag{86}$$

l being the mean distance between the two atom centres in the Cl_2 molecule. From the data of the Raman spectra, it is calculated that

$$A = 0 \cdot 153 \times \frac{\sin^2 \frac{1}{2}\theta}{\lambda^2}, \tag{87}$$

λ being measured in A. For Cu $K\alpha$ radiation ($\lambda = 1\cdot54$ A.) and for $\theta = 120°$, A is approximately equal to $0\cdot046$. Thus, the temperature correction at this angle is only about 5 % of the periodic part of the scattered intensity, and it may therefore easily be within the limits of error of the measurement of the total scattered intensity.

In polyatomic molecules the displacements of the different atoms are not independent of one another. The molecule containing N atoms forms a system of N coupled oscillators. Any small vibration of the system can be expressed as a linear combination of $3N - 6$ normal vibrations. The frequencies of the normal vibrations may be derived from the data of Raman and infra-red spectra. According to wave-mechanical theories, it is then possible to calculate the quantities $\overline{\delta l_{ij}^2}$ from a knowledge of these frequencies. The calculations in practice are difficult and elaborate, but they have been made for the molecules CCl_4 and $SiCl_4$. Table III gives the values of $(\overline{\delta l_{ij}^2})^{\frac{1}{2}}$ for the distances C-Cl or Si-Cl and the distances Cl-Cl in these two molecules at three different temperatures.

TABLE III. (After James [110])

Tem-perature	$(\overline{\delta l_{C\text{-}Cl}^2})^{\frac{1}{2}}$ or $(\overline{\delta l_{Si\text{-}Cl}^2})^{\frac{1}{2}}$ in A.			$(\overline{\delta l_{Cl\text{-}Cl}^2})^{\frac{1}{2}}$ in A.		
	0° K.	373° K.	573° K.	0° K.	373° K.	573° K.
CCl_4	0·051	0·056	0·062	0·054	0·076	0·092
$SiCl_4$	0·043	0·049	0·056	0·061	0·098	0·120

This table shows that the amplitude of the zero-point energy vibrations is large. The increase of amplitude occurring between 0 and 373° K., and between 373 and 573° K. is in comparison rather small. The major part of the temperature effect is therefore due to the zero-point indeterminacy of the position of the atoms in the molecule.

Fig. 55 represents the quantities $e^{-A_{ij}}$, in terms of $(\sin \tfrac{1}{2}\theta)/\lambda$, calculated for the Cl-Cl and C-Cl distances in CCl_4 at 300° C., according to equation (85) and using the data of Table III. Up to $(\sin \tfrac{1}{2}\theta)/\lambda = 0.6$, the correction factors e^{-A} are not very different

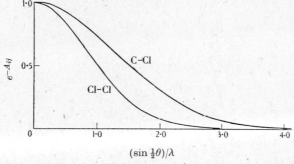

Fig. 55. The temperature correction factors $e^{-A_{ij}}$ for the molecule CCl_4 at 300° C.; above, for the C-Cl distances, below for the Cl-Cl distances. (After Pirenne(145).)

from unity, and the measurements accordingly are little affected by the temperature correction in this range. In the neighbourhood of $(\sin \tfrac{1}{2}\theta)/\lambda = 1.0$, however, the correction reduces the periodic intensity terms by about 30 % for the C-Cl distances and by 50 % for the Cl-Cl distances. As has been seen above, this effect has been experimentally observed at the fifth apparent maximum in an electron investigation of CCl_4. Although the matter has not been quantitatively investigated, the correction should make itself felt still more in the upper half of the range of $(\sin \tfrac{1}{2}\theta)/\lambda$, reaching up to about 2.0, which is covered by many electron investigations. At still higher values of $(\sin \tfrac{1}{2}\theta)/\lambda$, the importance of the undulations of the scattering curve must be expected to be drastically reduced. At $(\sin \tfrac{1}{2}\theta)/\lambda = 2.0$ the Cl-Cl interferences would be reduced by a factor 0.08, and at $(\sin \tfrac{1}{2}\theta)/\lambda = 3.0$, they would be reduced by a factor 0.002, which means that they would become practically invisible. The last remarks have only an indicative value, however, for equation (84) may not have a sufficient accuracy at large values of $(\sin \frac{1}{2}\theta)/\lambda$.

In the diffraction of X-rays by crystals, as is well known, the influence of the thermal and zero-point energy vibrations is very important.[†] It is of interest then to inquire why, contrary to what was at first expected, this is not also the case in the diffraction by gas molecules. The first reason is that the scattering pattern for crystals, consisting of sharp intense lines appearing on a light background, is very different from that of gases. A lowering of the intensity of these lines on account of the temperature effect is easily measurable. In the case of gases, on the contrary, an equivalent lowering of the broad maxima which appear superposed on to an intense background must naturally be less easy to detect. The second reason is that the atom displacements are smaller in molecules than in crystals. The theory of the temperature effect in crystals, as developed by Debye (30, 31) and Waller (168, 169), leads to a correction factor for the coherent intensity lines which is analogous to the factor $e^{-A_{ij}}$ for gas molecules. In the case of interference between the same kind of atoms, the characteristic values $2\overline{u_n^2}$, equal to twice the mean square of the atom displacements in the direction normal to the reflecting planes, replace the values $\overline{\delta l_{ij}^2}$ for gas scattering in formula (85). Now the amplitudes of the vibrations are much greater in the case of crystals, as is shown by Table IV, which gives the values of $(\overline{\delta l_{ij}^2})^{\frac{1}{2}}$ and $(2\overline{u_n^2})^{\frac{1}{2}}$, and the interatomic distances, in the molecules Cl_2 and CCl_4 and in the crystal KCl, at a temperature of $17°$ C.

TABLE IV. (After van der Grinten (86))

Cl_2 gas	$l_{Cl\text{-}Cl} = 2 \cdot 0$ A.	$(\overline{\delta l_{Cl\text{-}Cl}^2})^{\frac{1}{2}} = 0 \cdot 044$ A.
CCl_4 gas	$l_{Cl\text{-}Cl} = 2 \cdot 86$ A.	$(\overline{\delta l_{Cl\text{-}Cl}^2})^{\frac{1}{2}} = 0 \cdot 069$ A.
KCl crystal	$l_{Cl\text{-}Cl} = 4 \cdot 4$ A.	$(2\overline{u_n^2})^{\frac{1}{2}} = 0 \cdot 21$ A.

In brief, the influence of thermal vibrations is less noticeable in X-ray diffraction by gases than by crystals, partly because the two kinds of scattering patterns are different and partly because the amplitude of the atomic vibrations is different in the two cases.

[†] See Chapter IV.

II. ROTATING GROUPS IN MOLECULES

Two groups of atoms united in a molecule by a single carbon-carbon bond may rotate around this bond as an axis. Diffraction methods may give quantitative information as to the extent of such rotations, because the amplitude of such atomic displacements is generally greater than in the case of vibrations. As an example, the results obtained by Ehrhardt [67] on 1.2-dichloroethane, $ClH_2C—CH_2Cl$, will be discussed. As will be seen later, the H atoms do not need to be taken into consideration in X-ray scattering and the molecules can be represented by the model of Fig. 56. The atoms marked C, C* and Cl* may be taken as a frame of reference. The problem is to determine the probability of finding the atom Cl at an arbitrarily chosen angle ϕ from the *trans* position.

The experimental diffraction curve has a general resemblance to the experimental curve obtained by the same author for *trans* dichloroethylene, $ClHC=CHCl$. It is therefore probable that the molecule $ClH_2C—CH_2Cl$ has approximately a *trans* configuration. Although agreement is obtained as far as the principal characteristics are concerned, discrepancies persist when curves calculated for rigid *trans* models of $ClH_2C—CH_2Cl$ are compared with the experimental curve. The cause of these discrepancies must be ascribed to thermal movements in the molecule.

The possibility of completely free rotation has to be ruled out, because the assumption of equal probability of finding the atom Cl at any angle ϕ leads to calculated curves incompatible with observation. The existence of a mixture of rigid *trans* and *cis* configuration must also be excluded on the same grounds, as well as another rigid model which had been suggested by van't Hoff and Wislicenus and in which the atom Cl is at an angle $\phi = 60°$ from the *trans* position, facing an H atom of the opposite $C^*H_2Cl^*$ group.

The only remaining possibility is a distribution function for the atom Cl presenting a maximum at $\phi = 0$. This means that the Cl atom would oscillate around the more stable *trans* position. Using Boltzmann-Maxwell statistics and the experimental value of the dipole moment of the molecule such a distribution function has been calculated. It is represented, at the boiling-point of the substance, by the full line in Fig. 57. This function allows the calculation of a scattering curve which agrees well with the experimental curve. A rotation of limited extent therefore occurs around the *trans* position in the molecule.

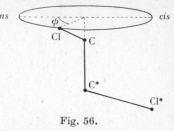

Fig. 56.

Attempts have been made, but in vain, to find a difference in the diffraction patterns obtained at temperatures differing by 100° C. The broken line in Fig. 57 represents the distribution function calculated for a temperature 100° C. higher than that corresponding to the full line. The theoretical scattering curve calculated using the new distribution also differs but very little from the first curve. This

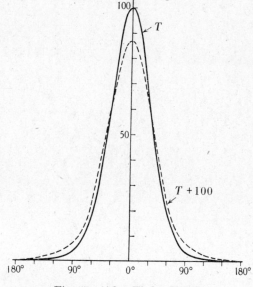

Fig. 57. (After Ehrhardt(67).)

is understandable if it is borne in mind that the Cl-Cl* distance is the only distance in the molecule which varies with the angle ϕ, the distance between C and C*, and the four distances between the C and Cl atoms remaining constant during the rotation. Moreover, the molecules in *trans* or nearly *trans* positions remain in the majority at both temperatures, the change in the number of molecular configurations corresponding to large values of the angle ϕ being relatively unimportant when the temperature is raised by $100°$.

In contradistinction to X-ray diffraction measurements, dipole moment measurements can detect a temperature effect in molecules such as ClH_2C—CH_2Cl; the experimental value of the moment varies with the temperature of the gas. In this connexion it must be observed that the dipole moment of molecules which are nearly in the *trans* configuration is very small. Accordingly, a small variation in the number of molecules having configurations notably different from the *trans* configuration, and having therefore large dipole moments, can produce an appreciable change in the mean value of the dipole moment of the molecules of the gas.

The diffraction of X-rays by some other molecules containing rotating groups, viz. 1.2-dichloropropane, ClH_2C—$CHCl$—CH_3, 1.3-dichloropropane, ClH_2C—CH_2—CH_2Cl and 1.5-dichloropentane, ClH_2C—CH_2—CH_2—CH_2—CH_2Cl, have been studied by Berger [7].[†]

A theoretical discussion of the influence on the electron diffraction patterns of atomic vibrations and of free or hindered rotation of molecular groups in molecules has been made by Debye [55], who discusses the results in terms of the 'radial distribution' [‡] method of analysis of the pattern.

[†] The CH_2Cl—CH_2Cl molecule has been investigated also by electron diffraction [4]. The 'visual method' of interpretation led to the result that there is a decided preference for the *trans* configuration. Internal rotation in the molecules BrH_2C—CH_2Br and ClH_2C—CH_2Br [5], and Cl_2HC—CH_2Cl [165] has also been studied by electron diffraction.

[‡] See Chapter xi.

CHAPTER IX

THE CHEMICAL BOND

IT has been emphasized in Chapter VI that all equations making use of the atomic scattering factors f—such as equations (65) and (84) —are valid only when the density of charge in each atom of the molecule is a function merely of the distance from the atomic centre, or, in other words, only when the electron clouds of all the atoms have spherical symmetry. Thus, since the chemical bond between two atoms is accompanied by a distortion of the electron atmospheres of these atoms, equations (65) and (84) are not strictly valid for calculating the scattering by actual molecules. The error involved is generally small, however, as has been pointed out by Debye [44], because the bonding electrons are outer electrons and therefore contribute but little to the scattering.

In the section on atomic scattering factors in Chapter I, it was pointed out that the outer electrons of the atom are distributed in a large and diffuse charge cloud in which important effects of destructive interference occur. For this reason, although the distribution of these electrons is less well known than that of the inner electrons, this uncertainty does not affect to any marked extent the accuracy of the calculations of the f factors. The insignificance of the outer electrons in the scattering curve of the atom is strikingly illustrated by the calculations of the scattering factors f of aluminium, for different states of ionization, made by James, Brindley and Wood, using Hartree's method. These authors write [108] that 'at all angles of scattering at which spectra can be obtained from the aluminium crystal, the values of f for the different possible states of ionization of the aluminium atom differ by less than the errors of the experimental determination of f'; this is shown in Fig. 58. It is evident, therefore, that if measurements are made at values of $(\sin \frac{1}{2}\theta)/\lambda$ which are not lower than, say, $0\cdot2$, the influence of the deformation of the outer electronic atmosphere by the chemical bond will be negligible, since it is then impossible even to see if the outer electrons are present or not. It must, however, be noted that if, in the case of a crystal, it is impossible to decide between such curves as these, it is not impossible in the case of a gas, because there no limitation exists *in principle* to measurements at very small scattering angles.

It follows that representing a molecule as a juxtaposition of atomic charge distributions, each of which possesses central symmetry, is, in general, a good approximation. On the other hand, if discrepancies were found between experimental curves and theoretical curves calculated on the above basis, they would be interesting because information might be gained from them about the distribution of the bonding electrons.[†] A theoretical

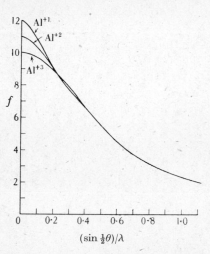

Fig. 58. Atomic scattering factors f calculated for the Al^+, Al^{++} and Al^{+++} ions by James, Brindley and Wood(108).

basis for such an investigation could be given by the extension to more complicated cases, for instance, to two-centre systems, of the Thomas-Fermi method which is used with success in the calculation of the electron distribution in free atoms. But attempts (106) in this direction have not been very successful. This is unfortunate because it is impossible, without independent assumptions, to derive uniquely from the scattering function the charge distribution in the molecule, as will be seen in Chapter XI.

NEON-LIKE MOLECULES

Interesting conclusions can be deduced from the experimental study of series of molecules which contain increasing numbers of bonding electrons, such as the series Ne, HF, H_2O, H_3N, H_4C. The above considerations concerning aluminium do not apply to such

[†] Hoffmann(102) has found some discrepancies between theory and experiment for the CO_2 molecule, but further experiments on monatomic gases would be necessary before definitely ascribing them to the chemical bond.

a very light atom as hydrogen, which is a constituent of four of the above molecules. In this atom there is not a sufficient density of electrons around the nucleus to give important X-ray coherent scattering at angles where the influence of the outer part of the atmosphere has become negligible: the whole electron atmosphere consists of one bonding electron only. For this reason, no hope exists of locating the hydrogen atom centre by X-ray diffraction. But, on the other hand, the molecules listed above are especially favourable cases for a study of the distribution of bonding electrons.

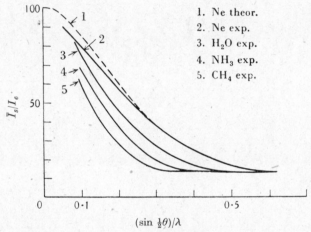

1. Ne theor.
2. Ne exp.
3. H_2O exp.
4. NH_3 exp.
5. CH_4 exp.

Fig. 59. X-ray scattering functions for Ne, H_2O, NH_3 and CH_4.
(After Thomer (162).)

All of them contain the same total number, 10, of electrons. On account of the differences in the arrangement of the positive charges in the molecule, the spatial distribution of this electronic charge must be expected to vary from molecule to molecule. These differences must have repercussions on the characteristics of the various scattering functions.

Fig. 59 represents the experimental scattering curves obtained by Thomer (162) for Ne, H_2O, NH_3 and CH_4, and the theoretical curve for Ne. (Other measurements on neon have been found to be in agreement with the theoretical curve, as seen in Chapter IV; the disagreement observed here at small angles is due to the use of imperfectly monochromatized radiation for the scattering by neon.)

The ordinates of all the curves have been taken as being equal at high scattering angles, in order to adjust them to the same scale. This procedure finds its justification in the facts that, for values of $(\sin \frac{1}{2}\theta)/\lambda$ larger than 0·5, the incoherent intensity is predominant and tends in all cases towards $Z = 10$, and that the coherent intensity which persists originates almost exclusively from the inner K electrons, which are not influenced by the presence of the H atoms. For θ tending to zero, all scattering functions should tend towards $Z^2 = 10^2 = 100$, but measurements were not made at very small angles.

Going from Ne to CH_4, the scattering functions are observed to become steeper and steeper. It must be expected that the less concentrated the electrons around the central nucleus, the steeper the corresponding scattering function will be. It can therefore be concluded that the electronic atmosphere is more and more diffuse when one goes from Ne to CH_4, that is, when the number of positive nuclei in the molecule becomes larger.

At values of $(\sin \frac{1}{2}\theta)/\lambda$ larger than 0·35, the molecules scatter X-rays in the same way as if they were free O, N or C atoms, but at smaller angles marked differences exist, and Thomer has made a quantitative discussion of the shape of the curves in this region. Representing the H_2O molecule by a juxtaposition of spherically symmetrical O and H atoms, according to equation (65) of Chapter VI (interference-like treatment), gives better agreement with measurement than considering it as an isolated O atom and thus disregarding the H atoms altogether. (The curve calculated by this interference-like treatment presents neither maxima nor inflexion points because the interatomic distances are too small in comparison with the size of the electronic atmospheres of the atoms.) The curve calculated in this way, however, is too steep, and the same state of affairs exists for the other molecules. This means that the O-H, N-H and C-H interferences are less marked than is implied by this treatment. The molecules resemble more closely the neon atom than is assumed in the juxtaposition model, that is, the H electrons must enter to some extent into the atmosphere of the central atom. This conclusion is in agreement with findings based on the diffraction of light (158) by the same molecules.

It was therefore deemed advisable to try and represent the total electron atmosphere of these molecules as a centrally symmetrical cloud. For that purpose, use was made of the interpolation method, mentioned in Chapter I, which has been used by James and Brindley (109) for the calculation of atomic scattering factors which have not been directly calculated by Hartree's method. It was possible to choose the 'screening constant' s, which characterizes the field and gives a measure of the extension of the charge cloud, in such a way that the calculated curves fit closely the experimental curves. The question of the incoherent intensity scattered by these neon-like models was also discussed. The differences in the incoherent intensity scattered by the molecules H_2O, NH_3, CH_4 are very small; it was shown that the method of Heisenberg-Bewilogua for calculating this intensity has a sufficient accuracy.

Thomer points out that it is not *proved* that the charge distribution in these molecules is really spherically symmetrical, but only that the results of X-ray diffraction can be described by a spherically symmetrical model. This model gives a simple method for calculating the scattering factors of organic groups such as CH_3, CH_2, CH, NH_2, NH and OH. In practice all that is needed is to determine the screening constant s. In this connexion it must be noted that a good approximation is already obtained by using the s value of the central atom in the neutral state, and considering the H electrons as part of the atmosphere of this atom. This treatment is superior not only to the mere neglecting of the H atoms in the molecule, but also to the interference-like treatment, which involves a large amount of numerical calculation.

This method of calculation is evidently of practical importance in many X-ray investigations, such as the study of liquids. For technical details the reader is referred to Thomer's paper, which contains a study made on these lines of the diffraction curve of the C_6H_6 molecule.

CHAPTER X

THE USE OF X-RAY AND ELECTRON DIFFRACTION FOR THE DETERMINATION OF THE GEOMETRICAL STRUCTURE OF FREE MOLECULES[†]

WHEN fast electrons are scattered by gas molecules they give diffraction patterns analogous to those of X-ray diffraction. It has been seen in Chapter v that under usual conditions the intensity of interaction with matter is much greater in the case of electrons than in the case of X-rays. Electron diffraction photographs can be obtained with much shorter exposure times than X-ray photographs. The intensity of the outer part of electron diffraction patterns, however, decreases so rapidly with increasing angle that the very outer diffraction rings may be very weak. In X-ray diffraction, there is no such general decrease of the total scattered intensity with increasing angle, but this is of little avail in determining molecular structures, for, at high values of $(\sin \frac{1}{2}\theta)/\lambda$, the importance of the coherent, relative to the incoherent, radiation becomes very small. This not being the case in electron diffraction, this method is preferable for studying the angular variation of the coherent intensity at high values of $(\sin \frac{1}{2}\theta)/\lambda$, notwithstanding the faintness of the intensity in this region.

ATOMIC FACTORS f AND F

The atomic scattering factor f for X-rays has been defined in Chapter I. The corresponding atomic scattering factor F for electrons has been defined in Chapter v by the following equation:

$$F = \frac{Z - f}{\left(4\pi \dfrac{\sin \frac{1}{2}\theta}{\lambda}\right)^2}. \tag{88}$$

Equation (91) below, which gives the electron intensity scattered by a free molecule, is fundamentally similar to that for X-rays, f being replaced by F.

[†] See also Bewilogua (8, 11).

It is interesting for a given atom to compare the X-ray scattering factor f with the function $(Z-f)$, which represents the scattering power of the atom for electrons disregarding the factor

$$[4\pi(\sin\tfrac{1}{2}\theta)/\lambda]^{-2},$$

which is the same for all atoms and which can be eliminated experimentally (56,57). At increasing values of $(\sin\tfrac{1}{2}\theta)/\lambda$, destructive interferences in the electron atmosphere reduce more and more the X-ray scattering factor f of the atom. Now in electron diffraction the very same function f represents the screening of the electron atmosphere of the atom: it is therefore the screening, not the scat-

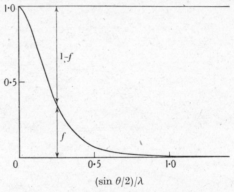

Fig. 60. Functions f and $1-f$ for the hydrogen atom.

tering power, which in this case decreases with increasing angle. While the atom therefore becomes less and less 'visible' for X-rays, it becomes more and more 'visible' for electrons, always disregarding the factor mentioned above. Fig. 60 represents the f and $1-f$ functions for the hydrogen atom. When $(\sin\tfrac{1}{2}\theta)/\lambda$ is greater than unity, the atom no longer scatters coherent X-ray radiation, while its scattering power for electrons becomes as great as if it were a naked nucleus. Hydrogen is an extreme case, and for heavier atoms the above situation will only be found at much higher values of $(\sin\tfrac{1}{2}\theta)/\lambda$, on account of the greater density of the inner electron atmosphere, especially of the K shell.

For X-rays the importance of each periodic term in equation (93) given below is determined by the product $f_i f_j$. In the corresponding equation (91) for electron diffraction it is determined by the products $F_i F_j$. It is therefore useful to compare with each other the scattering factors of different atoms, both for X-rays and for electrons. Fig. 37 of Chapter VI represents the X-ray scattering factor per electron, f/Z, for several atoms from H to Bi. It shows that the heavier the atom the slower is the decrease of f/Z. Referring to equation (88) defining F, this means that, while light atoms scatter X-rays proportionately less than heavy ones, they scatter electrons proportionately more than heavy ones. As an example, the case of the carbon and iodine atoms may be examined more closely. For two atoms A and B the ratios

$$K_X(A, B) = \frac{f_A Z_B}{f_B Z_A} \quad \text{for X-rays,} \tag{89}$$

and

$$K_E(A, B) = \frac{F_A Z_B}{F_B Z_A} \quad \text{for electrons,} \tag{90}$$

give the importance of the scattering power of A relative to B per unit nuclear charge. Fig. 61 shows that, except at $\theta = 0$, where $f = Z$ and $K_X(A, B) = 1$, the ratio $K_X(C, I)$ is smaller than unity,

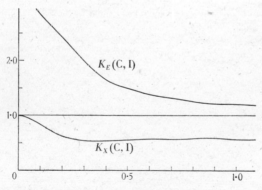

Fig. 61. The importance of the unit scattering power of the C atom, relative to the I atom, for X-rays (K_X) and for electrons (K_E). (After Pirenne(145).)

while $K_E(C, I)$ is greater than unity. This means that the atomic scattering factors are far from being proportional to the atomic numbers. At $(\sin \frac{1}{2}\theta)/\lambda = 0.6$, instead of being as 6 and 53, the atomic scattering factors of C and I for X-rays are as 6 and 92, and for electron rays they are as 6 and 39.

SHAPE OF THE X-RAY AND ELECTRON DIFFRACTION CURVES

Starting from the fundamental formula (56) and using again the assumption of spherical symmetry of the atoms constituting the molecule, which has allowed the use of the factors f in X-ray diffraction, the following expression is obtained for the scattering of rapid electrons by a free molecule [128]

$$\bar{I}_{s(E)} = \frac{I_0}{R^2} \frac{4}{a_H^2} \left[\underbrace{\sum_i \sum_j F_i F_j \frac{\sin x_{ij}}{x_{ij}}}_{\text{coherent}} + \underbrace{\sum_i \frac{Z_i S_i}{\left(4\pi \dfrac{\sin \frac{1}{2}\theta}{\lambda}\right)^4}}_{\text{incoherent}} \right]. \tag{91}$$

Using equation (88) this can be written

$$\bar{I}_{s(E)} = \frac{I_0}{R^2} \frac{4}{a_H^2} \frac{1}{\left(4\pi \dfrac{\sin \frac{1}{2}\theta}{\lambda}\right)^4} \left[\underbrace{\sum_i \sum_j (Z_i - f_i)(Z_j - f_j) \frac{\sin x_{ij}}{x_{ij}}}_{\text{coherent}} + \underbrace{\sum_i Z_i S_i}_{\text{incoherent}} \right]. \tag{92}$$

The symbols have their usual meanings, given above in connexion with equations (52) and (65) of Chapters v and vi. To take the temperature effect into account the products $F_i F_j$ in equation (91) should be multiplied by the factors $e^{-A_{ij}}$, in the same way as the products $f_i f_j$ are multiplied by these factors in equation (84) of Chapter viii.

Equation (92) for electron diffraction may be compared with the corresponding equation (65) for X-ray diffraction, reproduced here, without the relativistic correction Q:

$$\bar{I}_{s(X)} = \frac{I_0}{R^2} \frac{1 + \cos^2 \theta}{2} a_e^2 \left[\underbrace{\sum_i \sum_j f_i f_j \frac{\sin x_{ij}}{x_{ij}}}_{\text{coherent}} + \underbrace{\sum_i Z_i S_i}_{\text{incoherent}} \right]. \tag{93}$$

The most important difference between equations (92) and (93) is the presence in (92) of the coefficient $[4\pi(\sin \frac{1}{2}\theta)/\lambda]^{-4}$,[†] which determines the characteristic shape of the electron diffraction curve. On account of this factor, the decrease in intensity with increasing scattering angle θ is so rapid that, as a rule, neither maxima nor minima are observed, and the scattering function shows only points

† For $s = 0$, equation (92) would make $\bar{I}_s$ infinite, but [128] this formula is not valid for very small angles.

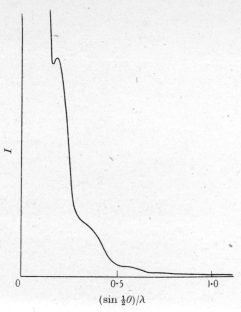

Fig. 62. Theoretical electron scattering function for the molecule CCl_4.
(After Pirenne (145).)

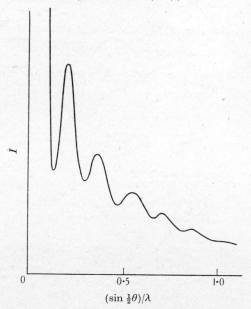

Fig. 63. Theoretical X-ray scattering function for the molecule CCl_4.
(After Pirenne (145).)

of inflexion. This is illustrated by Fig. 62 which gives the electron scattering function for CCl_4. The contrast with Fig. 63 is striking. The latter figure gives, for the same molecule, the X-ray scattering function, which presents five actual maxima. If, however, the influence of the factor $(\sin \tfrac{1}{2}\theta)^{-4}$ can be counterbalanced, equation (92) becomes essentially reduced to the expression between square brackets. Then the scattering function shows actual maxima which may even be more prominent than in the case of X-rays, on account of the difference, discussed above, in the behaviour of the functions $(Z-f)$ and f. By using a suitable rotating sector between the photographic plate and the scattering gas jet, P.P. Debye (56,57) has been able to obtain electron photographs showing actual maxima and minima, not only in the case of molecules such as CCl_4 (Fig. 64) but also in the case of NH_3 (Fig. 65). The latter case of course is especially interesting because this type of interference cannot be obtained by X-ray diffraction.[†]

Fig. 64. Comparison of the photometer records of electron diffraction photographs of the molecule CCl_4 obtained by using the ordinary method (a) and the sector method (b). (After P.P. Debye (56).)

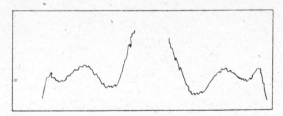

Fig. 65. Tracing of the photometer record of an electron diffraction photograph of the molecule NH_3 obtained by using the sector method. (After P.P. Debye (57).)

[†] On the sector method see also Debye (52), Yearian (181), Finbak (185), Finbak, Hassel and Ottar (184) and Bauer (3).

The use of such a method in the study of electron diffraction by gases was first suggested by Finbak (183).

INFLUENCE OF THE CHEMICAL BOND

It has been shown in Chapter IX that, in X-ray diffraction, the influence of the chemical bond—and, more generally, the scattering by the outer electrons—is appreciable only at small values of $(\sin \frac{1}{2}\theta)/\lambda$. The same applies to electron diffraction, since under conditions where the X-ray factor f can be used, the electron factor $Z-f$ can also be used. But the error at small scattering angles due to the chemical bond is likely to be more important for electrons than for X-rays. For, at small values of $(\sin \frac{1}{2}\theta)/\lambda$, the scattering factors f do not differ much from Z, so that, for the same absolute error in f, the percentage error will be greater in $(Z-f)$ than in f; for example, if $f = 0.9Z$, a one per cent difference in f makes a ten per cent difference in $(Z-f)$. It follows that for studying the distribution of the outermost electrons, electron diffraction may be a more sensitive method than X-ray diffraction.

For shorter and shorter wave-lengths, electron scattering tends towards the 'Rutherford scattering', which is due to the nuclei alone, but actually this limit is reached only at very high values of $(\sin \frac{1}{2}\theta)/\lambda$, except in the particular case of the hydrogen atom. In the range of most electron diffraction measurements, although the influence of the chemical bond, which involves the outermost electrons of the atom, is very small, the screening, which is due to the entire electron atmosphere, generally remains important. In X-ray diffraction, the influence of the chemical bond is also usually negligible and, except for very light atoms, the radiation in effect is scattered by the more compact inner electron shells. These constitute a spherically symmetrical system the centre of which coincides with the position of the nucleus.[†] As electrons are scattered by the atomic nucleus, screened by the very same electron shells, no discrepancy must be expected between the results given by the two diffraction methods.

Careful measurements on CCl_4 made by Degard, Piérard and van der Grinten [58] have shown that X-ray diffraction and electron diffraction actually lead to the same values of the interatomic distances in the molecule. The value of 2.86 A. for the Cl-Cl distance can be considered to be exact within limits of error of ± 0.01 A. [50].

[†] On this subject see also Stuart [159].

The location of such a light atom as the hydrogen atom is possible by electron diffraction, as has been seen above. As an example, the scattering of electrons by the H_2O molecule may be considered. Two approximations to the $(Z-f)$ factors can be made: either the three atoms forming the molecule are considered to be surrounded by the same electron atmospheres as if they were free (approximation I), or the molecule is represented as made of two naked H nuclei and a neon-like central atom according to Chapter IX (approximation II). Fig. 66 gives the value of the ratios $K_E(H, O)$, defined by equation (90), according to approximations I and II. When $(\sin \frac{1}{2}\theta)/\lambda$ is less than 0·4, the difference between approximations I and II is very

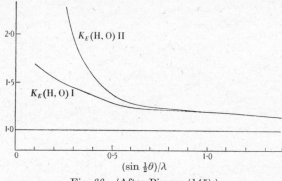

Fig. 66. (After Pirenne (145).)

great: this region should be used for studying the chemical bond. Beyond 0·8, approximations I and II are practically the same: the K electrons of the O atom are the only ones still giving effective screening. Between 0·4 and 0·8 there are differences, but they are not very important. As it is likely that some electronic screening remains around the H nuclei in this region, even if it is only due to the electron atmosphere of the O atom, approximation II is probably an exaggeration and one can have confidence in approximation I. Accordingly, at values of $(\sin \frac{1}{2}\theta)/\lambda$ above 0·4, ordinary scattering factors can be used in the calculations as a formal representation. For all molecules, therefore, even those containing hydrogen atoms, the electron diffraction calculations can be made using equation (91), that is, using for all atoms the scattering factors F defined by equation (88); this approximation, however, becomes unreliable at small diffraction angles.

THE LOCATION OF LIGHT ATOMS IN MOLECULES
CONTAINING BOTH LIGHT AND HEAVY ATOMS

The influence of the size of the atoms and of the distance between them in the diffraction of X-rays by a diatomic molecule has been discussed in Chapter VI. A molecule such as F_2, in which the electron atmospheres are diffuse and the interatomic distance is short, will give diffraction patterns much less favourable to the determination of the interatomic distance than the molecule Br_2, in which the distance Br-Br is greater than F-F and in which the electron atmospheres are more concentrated. Now it must be observed that in equations (91) and (93) the quantities that matter in this connexion are *products* of scattering factors, not scattering factors taken separately. A molecule such as ICl probably will give nearly as good a pattern as Br_2, although one of the atoms it contains is three times lighter than the other. It is evident, however, that if one of the atoms has a scattering factor which becomes vanishingly small as soon as the influence of the chemical bond becomes negligible, as would be the case for HBr, measurement of the interatomic distance by X-ray diffraction is impossible. On the other hand, measurement by electron diffraction of such distances as H-Br always remains possible, since the scattering of electrons by the H atom never becomes vanishingly small in comparison with the scattering by heavier atoms.

In polyatomic molecules, the importance of each distance l_{ij} is given by the product $f_i f_j$ or $F_i F_j$. Distances between heavy and heavy, between heavy and light, between light and light atoms are of decreasing importance. As examples of molecules containing atoms of different weights, the case of the chloromethanes may be examined. In the electron investigation of the molecule CH_3Cl, the H-H distances are not important, but the three H-Cl distances are by no means negligible; the factor

$$\frac{3F_H F_{Cl}}{F_C F_{Cl}} = \frac{3(1-f_H)}{6-f_C},$$

which gives their importance relative to that of the C-Cl distance, is equal to $3 \times 0.96/4.6 = 0.64$ for $(\sin \frac{1}{2}\theta)/\lambda = 0.6$. Moreover, the undulations due to these H-C distances will be relatively sharp, since they are longer than the C-Cl distance. It follows that the C-Cl value obtainable by electron diffraction alone depends to an appreciable extent on the assumptions which are made about the position of the H atoms in the molecule. And assumptions about the H atoms have to be made because the parameters are too numerous to be all easily determined using only electron diffraction. Now if X-ray diffraction is used together with electron diffraction, the conditions are more favourable, for the H atoms are 'invisible' in the X-ray method, which thus should give without ambiguity the C-Cl distance, only parameter left in this case. Once the C-Cl distance is known, it should be possible to locate the H atoms by electron diffraction measurements.

In the case of X-ray diffraction, the molecule CH_2Cl_2 can be considered as a CCl_2 group, the two C-Cl distances having an importance, relative to the Cl-Cl distance, equal to $2f_C f_{Cl}/f_{Cl}^2 = 0.5$. This case is more favourable to the determination of the valency angle Cl-C-Cl than the case of the molecule $CHCl_3$, where the three C-Cl distances have, relative to the three Cl-Cl distances, an importance equal only to 0.25. In CCl_4 the importance of the four C-Cl relative to the six Cl-Cl is lower still, 0.17 (always for $(\sin \frac{1}{2}\theta)/\lambda = 0.6$).

These examples show that the presence of heavy atoms does not necessarily render uncertain the location of the light atoms in a molecule. This occurs only when the heavy atoms are present in such number that their mutual distances become of predominant importance in the diffraction formula. Far from being unfavourable, the presence of one single heavy atom in a molecule may, on the contrary, emphasize the position of the light ones, as is the case, for instance, for the Cl atom in CH_3Cl, or in molecules such as $CH_2 = CHCl$.

In the case of the CH_2Cl_2 molecule, supposing that the C-C and Cl-Cl distances, and therefore the valency angle, have been measured by X-ray diffraction, the electron diffraction investigation may give indications about the position of the H atoms. Here there are one Cl-Cl, two C-Cl and four Cl-H distances, the importance of which is respectively 1, 0.84 and 0.36. In the molecule $CHCl_3$ the importance of the three Cl-Cl, the three C-Cl and the three Cl-H distances is respectively 1, 0·42 and 0·09. Hence the location of the H atom is scarcely possible here—but conversely, the importance of making a correct assumption about the position of the H atom is small.

It follows from this discussion that there is a distinct possibility of determining the complete structure of molecules such as CH_3Cl and CH_2Cl_2 entirely by diffraction methods without making any arbitrary assumptions—except, perhaps, about the symmetry of the molecule. This should be attempted using *both* X-ray diffraction and electron diffraction. It is also clear that the accuracy of inter-atomic distance measurements must be critically examined in each particular case, for the same atom may be easy to locate in one molecule, and difficult or impossible to locate in another.

TEMPERATURE EFFECT

The maxima of X-ray scattering functions are most prominent at low values of $(\sin \frac{1}{2}\theta)/\lambda$, that is, precisely where the effect of molecular vibrations is smallest. The temperature effect accordingly is not important in the use of X-ray diffraction for determining molecular structures. In electron diffraction, the outer maxima of the pattern are more important than in X-ray diffraction, and they have the advantage of being more sensitive to changes in the parameters characterizing the structure of the molecule. Unfortunately, in this region of large $(\sin \frac{1}{2}\theta)/\lambda$, the temperature correction is important and difficult to calculate. Complications which may arise from the temperature effect in the determination of the structure of polyatomic molecules by electron diffraction have been discussed by the writer (145).

In a general way, it must be borne in mind that, although the coherent intensity always remains important in electron diffraction, the periodic terms of this intensity may be drastically reduced at high angles on account of the temperature effect. These are the terms representing the interatomic interferences. As far as the determination of the interatomic distances in molecules is concerned, therefore, it would be quite misleading to draw a sharp contrast between the scattering of electrons by point-like atomic nuclei and the scattering of X-rays by diffuse electron atmospheres. This would be to forget that the indeterminacy in the position of the nuclei—the extent of which is not often well known—eventually reduces the sharpness of the interferences in a way similar to that in which the diffuseness of the electron atmospheres reduces the X-ray scattering factors f.

On the other hand, it is probable that electron diffraction will give information about the indeterminacy in the position of the atoms in molecules, especially when the new sector technique (56,57,3) which is being developed for this purpose is used (55).

CONCLUSION

X-ray diffraction and electron diffraction by gas molecules are methods which differ in the information they are able to give about the molecular structure. It is impossible to locate the hydrogen nuclei using X-ray diffraction, but this is possible using electron diffraction. In some cases the use of both diffraction methods may be necessary and sufficient for determining completely the structure of the molecule, including the position of the H atoms. In all cases where precision is needed, the use of both methods is clearly advisable for purposes of mutual control of the results, since both methods are capable of a high accuracy.

CHAPTER XI

FOURIER ANALYSIS OF INTERFERENCE MEASUREMENTS OF FREE MOLECULES

For the determination of the structure of free molecules whose X-ray or electron scattering functions are known, the most obvious method is a simple one of trial and error. Molecular models are assumed and the corresponding angular distribution of intensity calculated, using appropriate atomic scattering factors. The model giving a scattering function in agreement with the measured scattering function is taken as correct. This procedure alone is used in X-ray diffraction and it is much used in electron diffraction measurements.

The Fourier analyses used by Bragg for crystals, and by Compton for monatomic gases (Chapter IV), and which deduce from intensity measurements the charge distribution in the lattice unit-cell and the atom respectively, cannot be applied to the case of polyatomic molecules. The experimental result consists here of the mean value of *intensities* which have different angular distribution for different orientations of the molecule. In the case of a crystal which is kept in a given orientation the question of taking the mean of the intensity does not arise. In the atom the electron distribution is assumed to be spherically symmetrical, so that here again no mean has to be taken.

A method for determining directly the interatomic distances in molecules was described in 1935 by Pauling and Brockway [137]. This method, called by its authors the 'radial distribution' method, is used in the following way: A Fourier analysis of the angular distribution of the experimentally measured intensities yields a function $D(r)$ which must present maxima for the values of r which are equal to the distances between any pair of nuclei in the molecule. In practice the method has given values which are often in good agreement with the results of the older method. A theoretical discussion of the method and an examination of its applicability to X-ray measurements have been made by Debye and the writer [51].

DEFINITION OF THE FUNCTION $D(r)$

(a) **X-ray diffraction.** In Chapter VI a general formula has been given for the mean intensity $\bar{I}_s$ scattered by the electron cloud of a free molecule which takes successively all possible orientations in space. This formula will be used here as a starting point. For the case of unpolarized primary radiation, it may be written

$$\frac{\bar{I}_s}{I_0} = \frac{a_e^2}{R^2} \frac{1 + \cos^2\theta}{2} \iint \rho_1 \rho_2 \frac{\sin ksr}{ksr} dV_1 dV_2. \tag{94}$$

ρ_1 and ρ_2 are the electron densities (mean number of electrons in unit volume) in volume elements dV_1 and dV_2 respectively; r is the distance between the volume elements dV_1 and dV_2; $k = 2\pi/\lambda$ and $s = 2\sin\frac{1}{2}\theta$. A large number of molecules is always investigated at a time, but if the density of the gas is not high, the actual intensity scattered by the molecules is obtained simply by multiplying the intensity $\bar{I}_s$ of equation (94) by N, the number of molecules, as has been seen in Chapter VII.

The double integral of equation (94) may be calculated in the following way. A volume element dV_1 is arbitrarily selected in the molecule. Around this element taken as centre, two spheres, of radii r and $r + dr$, are placed. Then, if $d\Omega_2$ is the element of solid angle, an integration can be performed over this variable. The result of this first step is

$$\frac{\sin ksr}{ksr} r^2 dr \int \rho_2 d\Omega_2. \tag{95}$$

The central volume element dV_1, which so far has been considered immobile, is now given successively all possible positions in the molecule while the distance r remains constant. This second step gives

$$\frac{\sin ksr}{ksr} r^2 dr \int \rho_1 dV_1 \int \rho_2 d\Omega_2 = D(r) \frac{\sin ksr}{ksr} 4\pi r^2 dr, \tag{96}$$

where $D(r)$ is a 'density function' which depends only upon the arbitrarily chosen distance r. Finally the average intensity $\bar{I}_s$ is given by the following equation, which takes the place of equation (94):

$$\frac{\bar{I}_s}{I_0} = \frac{a_e^2}{R^2} \frac{1 + \cos^2\theta}{2} \int_0^\infty D(r) \frac{\sin ksr}{ksr} 4\pi r^2 dr. \tag{97}$$

The integration is thus made complete by giving r all possible values from zero to infinity.

The density function D introduced in this way is all that can in principle be deduced from the measurement of the angular distribution of the scattered intensity. It has the dimensions cm.$^{-3}$, hence the name it is given here. The way the function D is obtained may be summarized as follows:

We place a sphere of radius r anywhere in the molecule. At the surface of this sphere we determine the mean surface density of electrons. Then we move the sphere throughout the whole molecule and we take the sum of all the surface densities, which have different values for different positions of the sphere, each term of this sum being given a weight equal to the electron density at the centre of the corresponding sphere. The electron density obtained in this way, considered from the point of view of its dependence upon r, is the density function $D(r)$:

$$D(r) = \int \rho_1 dV_1 \int \rho_2 \frac{d\Omega_2}{4\pi}. \tag{98}$$

(*b*) **Electron diffraction.** Calculations can be made along the same lines for the diffraction of fast electrons by a free molecule. The only difference is that the density ρ refers here not to the electrons only, but to all the electric charges, including the nuclear charges in the molecule. The quantity ρ represents the mean number of elementary charges in unit volume, this number being positive or negative according to the sign of the charge. To be quite accurate, the same should have been done in the calculation of the diffraction of X-rays, but in that case the scattered amplitudes are inversely proportional to the mass of the scattering particles, and for that reason the influence of the nuclei can in practice be neglected. E being the energy of one of the incident electrons, the following result is obtained:

$$\frac{\bar{I}_s}{I_0} = \frac{(e^2/E)^2}{R^2} \frac{1}{s^4} \int_0^\infty D(r) \frac{\sin ksr}{ksr} 4\pi r^2 dr. \tag{99}$$

The factors in front of the integral may be compared with those of equation (50) in Chapter v. The factor e^2/E has the dimensions of a length and takes the place of the electron radius a_e of equation (94). The density function $D(r)$ is defined by

$$D(r) = \int \rho_1 dV_1 \int \rho_2 \frac{d\Omega_2}{4\pi}, \tag{100}$$

which is the same as equation (98) except for the fact that ρ here signifies the number of elementary charges in unit volume, all charges being taken into account together with their signs.

The intensity formula (97) or (99) has a formal analogy with formula (78) of Chapter VII, which was given by Zernike and Prins (182) and used by Menke (126) to determine the atomic arrangement in monatomic liquids. This analogy was used by Pauling and Brockway in the derivation of the radial distribution method, but actually the meaning of the density functions is not the same in the two cases.

It may be written, for X-rays,

$$\frac{\bar{I}_s}{I_0} = N \frac{a_e^2}{R^2} \frac{1 + \cos^2\theta}{2} B_X\left(\frac{s}{\lambda}\right), \tag{101}$$

for electron rays,

$$\frac{\bar{I}_s}{I_0} = N \frac{(e^2/E)^2}{R^2} \frac{1}{s^4} B_E\left(\frac{s}{\lambda}\right). \tag{102}$$

Assuming that in diffraction experiments referring to N molecules it has been possible to separate experimentally the coherent part of the intensity from the incoherent background, the quantities B, which are functions of the scattering angle θ, may be considered to be experimentally known. According to Fourier's theorem the density function D can then be obtained by calculating the integral

$$rD(r) = 2 \int_0^\infty \frac{s}{\lambda} B\left(\frac{s}{\lambda}\right) \sin\left(2\pi r \frac{s}{\lambda}\right) d\left(\frac{s}{\lambda}\right). \tag{103}$$

Now in the calculations relating to their experiments, Pauling and Brockway do not really follow the procedure defined by equation (103). First the separation of the coherent from the incoherent intensity is not carried out. Secondly no actual intensity curves are determined, but instead the intensity and position of the interference rings are visually estimated, whereby on account of a known physiological effect, intensity maxima are seen, although they do not exist. The estimated intensities, for any chosen value of r, are then multiplied by the corresponding values of $s/\lambda \sin(2\pi r s/\lambda)$ and added to one another. This procedure generally replaces the integration. As it is repeated for different values of r, the curve so obtained, plotted against r, is considered to be a sufficient substitute for the real curve $rD(r)$. In fact, this curve shows maxima for certain values of the distance r, and these special distances are considered to be the distances of the nuclei in the molecule. Notwithstanding the roughness of this procedure, very good results have been obtained. It is therefore interesting to calculate, for a particular case, the behaviour of curves $D(r)$ such as would be obtained by an exact treatment of perfect experimental results, and to see how accurately the positions of their maxima then coincide with the internuclear distances.

THEORETICAL CALCULATION OF THE DENSITY FUNCTION FOR A DIATOMIC MOLECULE

(a) **X-rays.** The same kind of imaginary diatomic molecule as has been used in Chapter VI to study the influence of the diffuseness of the electron clouds on the scattering function will be used here. The two nuclei of the molecule are situated at a distance l from each other. Each nucleus is surrounded by an electron cloud having the following density distribution:

$$\rho = \frac{z}{\pi^{\frac{3}{2}} a^3} e^{-u^2/a^2}. \tag{104}$$

This particular form of the function ρ is chosen for convenience in the calculations; it is the same as in equation (62) of Chapter VI. The parameter a characterizes the size of the electron cloud. The distance from the nucleus is called u, and the numerical factor is chosen in such a way that the whole atom contains z electrons.

According to the procedure outlined in the preceding paragraph, the electron density on the surface of a sphere of radius r, the centre of which is at a distance v from the nucleus, is first to be calculated (Fig. 67). Putting

$$u^2 = r^2 + v^2 - 2rv \cos\alpha, \tag{105}$$

the result for the electrons belonging to one nucleus is

$$\int \rho_2 \frac{d\Omega_2}{4\pi} = \frac{z}{\pi^{\frac{3}{2}} a^3} \frac{1}{2} \int e^{-(r^2+v^2-2rv\cos\alpha)/a^2} \sin\alpha\, d\alpha$$

$$= \frac{z}{\pi^{\frac{3}{2}} a^3} e^{-(r^2+v^2)/a^2} \frac{\sinh(2rv/a^2)}{2rv/a^2}. \tag{106}$$

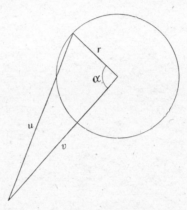

Fig. 67.

If the distance of the centre of the sphere from the first nucleus is called v_1, and the distance from the other nucleus v_2, the result for the whole molecule is

$$K = \int \rho_2 \frac{d\Omega_2}{4\pi}$$

$$= \frac{z}{\pi^{\frac{3}{2}} a^3} e^{-r^2/a^2} \left[e^{-v_1^2/a^2} \frac{\sinh(2rv_1/a^2)}{2rv_1/a^2} + e^{-v_2^2/a^2} \frac{\sinh(2rv_2/a^2)}{2rv_2/a^2} \right]. \tag{107}$$

Now K multiplied by the density ρ in the volume element dV at the centre of the sphere must be integrated over the whole of space. The density function $D(r)$ is therefore given by

$$D(r) = \frac{z}{\pi^{\frac{3}{2}} a^3} \int (e^{-v_1^2/a^2} + e^{-v_2^2/a^2}) K\, dV. \tag{108}$$

The integrals can be directly calculated, and finally the following relation is obtained:

$$D(r) = \frac{2z^2}{(2\pi)^{\frac{3}{2}} a^3} e^{-r^2/2a^2} \left[1 + e^{-l^2/2a^2} \frac{\sinh(rl/a^2)}{rl/a^2} \right]. \tag{109}$$

This equation may be written

$$D(r) = \frac{z^2}{(2\pi)^{\frac{3}{2}} a^3} \left[2e^{-r^2/2a^2} + \frac{e^{-(l-r)^2/2a^2}}{rl/a^2} - \frac{e^{-(l+r)^2/2a^2}}{rl/a^2} \right], \quad (110)$$

which shows more clearly how the distance $r = l$, corresponding to the internuclear distance, acquires a special importance when the ratio l/a is large.

Figs. 68, 69, and 70 represent density functions D plotted against r/l as abscissae, the factor $\dfrac{z^2}{(2\pi)^{\frac{3}{2}} a^3} \dfrac{l^2}{a^2}$ being omitted. The three curves

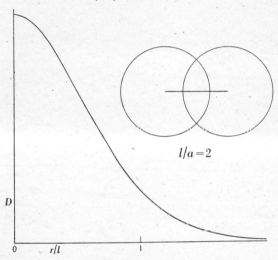

$l/a = 2$

D

$0 \quad r/l \quad 1$

Fig. 68. (After Debye and Pirenne (51).)

correspond respectively to the assumptions $l/a = 2$, $l/a = 4$ and $l/a = 8$. In order to visualize the size of the electron clouds, the molecules are represented schematically beside the D functions, in the same way as in Fig. 36 of Chapter VI. At the surface of the spheres of radius $a\sqrt{2}$ which are drawn around the nuclei, the electron density relating to one atom is reduced to $1/e^2 = 1/7\cdot39$ of its value at the centre of the atom. The assumption $l/a = 8$ approximately corresponds to the case of the chlorine molecule. In the first two cases, $l/a = 2$ and $l/a = 4$, the D curves show no maximum at all. Only in the last case, $l/a = 8$, does a maximum appear. Although the electrons here are more concentrated around the nuclei, the position of the maximum of the D function does not coincide with the inter-nuclear distance $r = l$, but is displaced by 1·5 % towards the smaller values of r/l, as can be easily calculated.

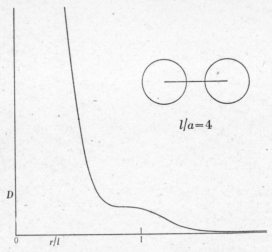

Fig. 69. (After Debye and Pirenne (51).)

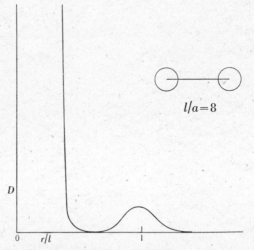

Fig. 70. (After Debye and Pirenne (51).)

It must be concluded from this discussion that *for exact deter-minations of interatomic distances in molecules, the D method in the case of X-ray interferences does not appear to be suitable.*

(b) **Electron rays.** The same imaginary diatomic molecule is again used in this case. The density of negative electric charge in each atom, the sign of the charge being taken into account, is represented by

$$\rho = -\frac{z}{\pi^{\frac{3}{2}} a^3} e^{-u^2/a^2}. \tag{111}$$

The density of positive charge is represented in a similar way by

$$\rho = +\frac{z}{\pi^{\frac{3}{2}} a_0^3} e^{-u^2/a_0^2}. \tag{112}$$

Taking again a sphere of radius r, the centre of which is situated at a distance v_1 from nucleus 1, and at a distance v_2 from nucleus 2, the mean density of charge on this sphere can be immediately obtained, using what has been found in paragraph (a):

$$\int \rho_2 \frac{d\Omega}{4\pi} = f_0(v_1) - f(v_1) + f_0(v_2) - f(v_2), \tag{113}$$

where $f(v)$ represents the function

$$f(v) = \frac{z}{\pi^{\frac{3}{2}} a^3} e^{-(r^2+v^2)/a^2} \frac{\sinh (2rv/a^2)}{2rv/a^2}, \tag{114}$$

while $f_0(v)$ is the same function where a is replaced by a_0. Similarly, ρ can be written

$$\rho = g_0(v_1) - g(v_1) + g_0(v_2) - g(v_2), \tag{115}$$

$g(v)$ representing the function

$$g(v) = \frac{z}{\pi^{\frac{3}{2}} a^3} e^{-v^2/a^2}. \tag{116}$$

Now ρ, given by equation (115), must be multiplied by the value of the integral (113) and then integrated over the whole of space. The integrations can all be performed, the final result being

$$D(r) = \frac{z^2}{(2\pi)^{\frac{3}{2}}} \Bigg[2\frac{1}{a_0^3} e^{-r^2/2a_0^2} \bigg(1 + e^{-l^2/2a_0^2} \frac{\sinh (rl/a_0^2)}{rl/a_0^2} \bigg)$$

$$+ 2\frac{1}{a^3} e^{-r^2/2a^2} \bigg(1 + e^{-l^2/2a^2} \frac{\sinh (rl/a^2)}{rl/a^2} \bigg)$$

$$- 4\bigg(\frac{2}{a^2+a_0^2}\bigg)^{\frac{3}{2}} e^{-r^2/(a^2+a_0^2)} \bigg(1 + e^{-l^2/(a^2+a_0^2)} \frac{\sinh (2rl/(a^2+a_0^2))}{2rl/(a^2+a_0^2)} \bigg) \Bigg]. \tag{117}$$

The limiting case of infinitely small nuclei will first be examined. In that case $a_0 = 0$ and the first term in equation (117) is zero everywhere except for $r = 0$ and for $r = l$, at which points infinitely high and infinitely sharp maxima are produced. In order to derive the mean scattered intensity from the density function, according to equation (99), $D(r)$ must be multiplied by $(\sin ksr)/ksr \cdot 4\pi r^2 \, dr$ and the sum taken over all values of r. When this is carried out for the first term of equation (117), the result is

$$\int D(r)\frac{\sin ksr}{ksr} 4\pi r^2 dr = 2z^2\left[1+\frac{\sin ksl}{ksl}\right], \qquad (118)$$

which is as it should be, since it represents the interaction between two naked nuclei, that is, between two scattering points, as discussed in Chapter VI.

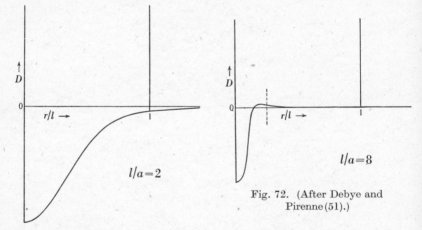

Fig. 72. (After Debye and Pirenne (51).)

Fig. 71. (After Debye and Pirenne (51).)

The second, positive, term of equation (117) corresponds to the interaction between electrons, and the third, negative, term to the interaction between nuclei and electrons. The behaviour of these terms again depends upon the choice of the ratios l/a. For the two cases $l/a = 2$ and $l/a = 8$ the curves representing the complete density functions D are drawn respectively in Figs. 71 and 72. The ordinate of these curves often assumes negative values; in the case of $l/a = 8$ there are weak maxima. The curves are smooth, except for the fact that—in contradistinction to the case of the X-ray D functions—infinitely high and sharp points stand on them at $r = 0$

and $r = l$. D takes negative values in the case of electron diffraction because, as can easily be proved [51],

$$\int D(r)\, 4\pi r^2 dr = 0, \tag{119}$$

in the case of a molecule in the neutral state.

In fact, the calculations must not be made taking a_0 as vanishingly small, for the position of the nuclei is not perfectly determinate, if only on account of their zero-point energy. This effect can be taken into consideration by giving a_0 a finite value. In Fig. 73, a new $D(r)$ curve is drawn for the ratios $l/a = 8$ and $l/a_0 = 50$, which should

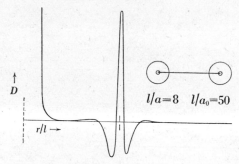

Fig. 73. (After Debye and Pirenne [51].)

approximately correspond to the conditions prevailing in the Cl_2 molecule. The figure shows two weak maxima at about $r/l = 0.8$ and $r/l = 1.2$; two minima nearer to $r/l = 1$, at about $r/l = 0.94$ and $r/l = 1.06$; and finally a sharp maximum at $r/l = 1$. Supplementary maxima, the positions of which do not correspond to inter-nuclear distances, are therefore present. It is, however, clear that in the case of electron diffraction the circumstances are much more favourable to the use of the density function method for the determination of internuclear distances than in the case of X-ray diffraction, on account of the role played by the atomic nuclei in the scattering of electrons.[†] It will also be noted that the width of the sharp peak of the D function depends upon the value of a_0, which characterizes the indeterminacy of the position of the nuclei in the molecule.

[†] For further discussion see Debye [53].

NEW INTERPRETATION OF THE FUNCTION $D(r)$ IN ELECTRON DIFFRACTION

A new and very simple interpretation of the function $D(r)$ in electron diffraction has been given by Debye [55]. In the ideal case of a molecule the scattering by which is purely nuclear, it can be shown that, if $P(r)\,dr$ is the probability that the distance between two of the nuclei, i and j, has a value between r and $r+dr$, the function $D(r)$, in the immediate neighbourhood of $r = l_{ij}$ (l_{ij} being the mean distance of the nuclei i and j), is

$$D(r) = \frac{\pi}{2} z_i z_j \frac{P(r)}{r}, \qquad (120)$$

z_i and z_j being the numbers of elementary charges contained in the nuclei i and j. The ordinate of the radial distribution curve D therefore represents essentially the probability of occurrence of the interatomic distance r in the molecule. Now, in the calculation of the scattering by an actual molecule, the screening by the electron atmosphere of the atom, which varies with the scattering angle θ, must be taken into account: the actual D curve then is not represented exactly by equation (120). The correction to be introduced, however, is of rather minor importance. Knowing the atomic factors f, it should therefore be possible to derive a curve corresponding to equation (120) from the actual D curve. Thus, according to this interpretation of the D function, if a curve corresponding to equation (120) can be derived from experiments with sufficient precision, it will give a direct quantitative picture of the displacements, rotations and vibrations, of the atoms inside the molecule.

The maxima of some of the D curves which have been derived up to now from electron diffraction experiments, with a view to determining intramolecular distances, are much less sharp than those of the theoretical curve discussed above. It does not appear certain, at least *a priori*, that the positions of such broad maxima must always coincide quite accurately with the positions which the true sharp maxima should occupy. But improvements are being made in the technique for recording intensities and they are bound to lead to a corresponding increase in the accuracy of the radial distribution curves. These presumably will then become capable of also giving quantitative information about the magnitude of the intramolecular motions (3, 185).

In conclusion, it may be pointed out that the D functions contain in principle all the information directly available from diffraction experiments on free molecules. According to equations (97) and (99), two different scattering systems having identical D functions —the actual existence of which is very unlikely—would scatter exactly the same intensity and be indistinguishable from the point of view of X-ray and electron diffraction. Strictly speaking, therefore, the actual charge distribution in the molecule cannot be determined using diffraction data only. In the determination of molecular structure, however, the knowledge of the chemical formula of the molecule generally gives enough additional knowledge to allow the location of the various atoms, as has been seen above, especially in Chapter VI.

CHAPTER XII

THE MEASUREMENT OF THE X-RAY SCATTERING FUNCTIONS OF GASES

TECHNICAL difficulties in the investigation of the diffraction of X-rays by gases are mainly due to the faintness of the scattered radiation. The utmost care must be exercised to suppress all parasitic radiation. When this is achieved, the accurate measurement of the scattered intensity is itself a difficult task.

Absolute measurements, that is, direct comparisons of the scattered to the incident intensity, have been made in a few cases.[†] In molecular structure determinations, only relative measurements of the intensities scattered at different angles are generally made. In such cases, correspondence between experimental and theoretical intensity curves is obtained by taking their ordinates as being equal at any chosen angle.

Fig. 74.

The angular distribution of the mean intensity scattered by free molecules for unpolarized primary radiation depends only upon the angle θ between the primary and secondary rays. The intensity distribution is symmetrical about the direction of the primary beam. The scattering function is therefore generally obtained by measuring the intensity scattered in a plane containing the primary beam. For instance, a cylindrical film can be used, the axis of the cylinder being perpendicular to the primary direction and passing through the scattering substance, as shown in Fig. 74. A movable recording device (such as an ionization chamber) which can successively assume different positions around the scattering substance can be used in place of the cylindrical film. Measurements may also

† For absolute measurements on argon (100) see Chapter IV; on polyatomic gases see Hoffmann(102) and Lu(120).

be made using a photographic plate perpendicular to the incident beam, a pattern of concentric rings being produced on the plate, as shown in Fig. 75, but this does not give a scattering function for all angles θ.

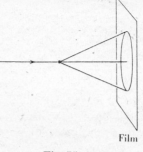

Fig. 75.

The method of X-ray diffraction by gases is analogous to the powder method of Debye-Scherrer for the diffraction of X-rays by a large number of very small crystals oriented at random. The first arrangement, shown in Fig. 74, is generally used for X-ray diffraction by gases,[†] as well as for X-ray powder photographs. The second arrangement, shown in Fig. 75, is used for electron diffraction by gases or by thin foils; in electron diffraction, the wave-lengths being shorter, a smaller angle range is adequate.

DIFFRACTION CELLS

Scherrer and Stäger (154) used an apparatus in which a thin jet of hot mercury vapour emerges through an orifice, passes freely through the air for a few millimetres, and is received in another tube below. X-ray diffraction photographs were obtained in about 20 hr., using filtered copper radiation, with exactly the same arrangement as if the vapour beam had been a powder cylinder.

In most experiments, however, the gas is contained in a closed cell. It might be thought that the vapour could be placed in a narrow thin-walled tube, as is done in the study of some powders, the gas scattering being found by subtracting the scattering by the empty tube from the total scattering. This is not practicable because, scattered X-ray intensities being roughly proportional to the mass of the scattering material, the scattering by the walls would be too intense. Cells possessing windows are used, but they are arranged in such a way that the radiation scattered by the window through which the primary beam passes cannot reach the

---

[†] The second arrangement, however, was used in the first experiment, made on CCl_4, which showed an interference maximum in the diffraction of X-rays by isolated molecules (40).

photographic film. The effective scattering volume then is smaller than the total volume of gas which scatters the primary radiation, the latter volume itself being smaller than the total gas volume. The effective scattering volume is limited at any angle θ, not by walls, but by the geometrical disposition of slits and screens in the cell. In such an arrangement, incident and scattered rays go through an appreciable thickness of gas, and the absorption by the gas must be taken into account. The total gas thickness traversed by the primary and secondary rays generally changes with scattering angle, and a correction for absorption must therefore be applied to the curve of the measured intensity.

Dependence of the intensity upon gas pressure. With increasing gas pressure inside the cell, the losses by absorption increase, as does the number of scattering molecules. There is

therefore at a certain pressure, which it is important to know, a maximum yield of scattered intensity. The case of the type of cell represented by Fig. 76 may be examined. The incident beam comes into the gas through the window A. The rays scattered, for instance, in the direction OB, pass through the slit O situated in the middle of the cell and traverse the gas thickness OB before reaching the window $FBDE$. When the scattering

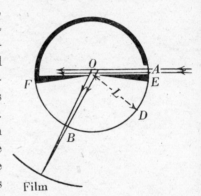

Fig. 76. (After Pirenne (144).)

volume V is irradiated with an incident beam of intensity I_0, it scatters an intensity proportional to the number of electrons it contains:

$$I_s = KI_0 VNC; \tag{121}$$

N is the number of electrons in one cubic centimetre of gas for a concentration C equal to unity. Strictly speaking, K changes from gas to gas but here it can be considered roughly as constant. The incident beam is weakened by absorption on its way from A to O, and the scattered beam on its way from O to B. Each time the loss can be taken into account by a factor $e^{-L\mu C}$, L being the radius of the cell, and μ the linear absorption coefficient for the gas at a concentration C equal to unity. The scattered intensity i which passes through the window $FBDE$, is therefore

$$i = KI_0\,VNCe^{-2L\mu C}. \quad (122)$$

This function has a maximum for

$$\mu C = \frac{1}{2L}. \quad (123)$$

There is accordingly for each substance an optimum concentration (100, 144). In order to be able to deal with the same function for all substances, it

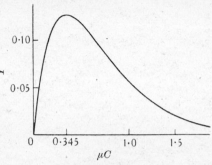

Fig. 77. The function $Y = \mu Ce^{-2\times1\cdot45\mu C}$. (After Pirenne (144).)

is convenient to consider, instead of i, the quantity

$$Y = \mu Ce^{-2L\mu C}$$

as a function of μC. Fig. 77 represents this function for the special case where $L = 1\cdot45$ cm. For a given gas and a given wave-length, at any pressure, the emerging intensity i is proportional to the ordinate Y corresponding to the particular value of C. To compare the intensity i for two different gases and wave-lengths, i.e. for different values N_1 and N_2 of N, and different values μ_1 and μ_2 of μ, the corresponding values of Y are multiplied by N_1/μ_1 and N_2/μ_2 respectively. This is only an approximation since K is not exactly a universal constant. Experimental verifications are available for cells of radii $1\cdot45$ and $5\cdot71$ cm. (144). For a cell of radius $1\cdot45$ cm., and for $SiHCl_3$ vapour at $100°$ C., the optimum pressure is $0\cdot43$ atm. for iron radiation ($1\cdot94$ A.), $0\cdot83$ atm. for copper radiation ($1\cdot54$ A.) and $7\cdot4$ atm. for molybdenum radiation ($0\cdot71$ A.). Using the latter radiation and a gas pressure of $4\cdot3$ atm., the writer (144) has been able to reduce the time of exposure, for crystal-reflected radiation, from 100 to 35 hr. for dark photographs, and to 8 hr. for light photographs. It may be pointed out that this is due to the simultaneous use of short wave-length X-rays and of a small-sized cell. Older experimental arrangements, which did not fulfil both of these conditions, gave a maximum increase of intensity of about 50 % only, instead of 200 %.

Parasitic radiation due to secondary and tertiary scattering. As has already been pointed out, the *secondary* radiation emitted by the cell window and walls is important. For instance, a mica entrance window can give dark spots of a Laue pattern superimposed upon the gas diffraction pattern. The geometrical construction of the cell must therefore be such that no radiation scattered by the window, or by the apparatus which absorbs the primary beam after gas diffraction, can interfere with the measurements. This makes measurements difficult at small scattering angles. Using a cell of the type represented by Fig. 76, measurements are limited to angles larger than the angle of the forward prism OF. At lower angles the intensity scattered by the window A passes through the diffraction slit O and is superimposed upon the gas pattern. The window A might be put farther back if it were desired to make measurements at smaller angles, but this would lead, among other inconveniences, to an increased absorption of the incident beam in the gas.

The intensity scattered by a given volume of gas is proportional to the concentration of the gas. Secondary radiation is scattered again by the gas and gives tertiary radiation, the intensity of which is therefore proportional to the square of the gas concentration (95). With increasing pressure this tertiary intensity accordingly increases much more rapidly than the secondary intensity which is to be measured. In general, however, it is still unimportant at pressures of a few atmospheres. This is due to the fact that the intensity of interaction of X-rays with gases is small. The gas which is adjacent to the scattering volume re-scatters only a very small fraction of the secondary radiation which passes through it, in the same way as only a very small part of the primary beam is scattered by the gas (144).[†] Similar reasoning shows that tertiary scattering originating in a thin window and in the cell walls is generally not disturbing.

Fluorescent radiation. The total loss in intensity suffered by an X-ray beam traversing matter is due only to a small degree to

---

[†] Evidently neither of these remarks holds for systems having a high density N of electrons, such as liquid benzene, for instance. They are also invalid for electron rays.

scattering, and to a much larger degree to true absorption. Absorption brings along with it emission of fluorescent radiation, the intensity of which is generally greater than that of the scattered radiation, as seen in Chapter III. For obtaining a high yield of scattered intensity, as explained above, a small absorption coefficient is desirable. The X-ray wave-length for this reason is generally chosen so that the absorption in the gas is low. This circumstance is conducive to a low fluorescence intensity, but it does not in any way render it negligible.

Fluorescent radiation, therefore, must be eliminated experimentally. This often can be done by using a suitable X-ray filter. This filter sometimes may be constituted by the cell window itself. A mica sheet 0·05 mm. thick, for instance, completely stops the fluorescent radiation of silicon and chlorine. When a substance such as $SiHCl_3$ is studied in a cell provided with such a mica window, using molybdenum radiation, less than 10 % of this radiation is absorbed by the mica, while the fluorescent radiation is completely prevented from reaching the photographic film (144).

Difficulties, however, may arise in some cases. It may happen that no sufficiently selective filter can be used, and at the same time that the K excitation of the atom cannot be avoided. Such is the case for the scattering of copper radiation by bromine (7). Bewilogua[†] has suggested the use in this case of an ionization chamber filled with a bromine compound. This chamber would let the bromine fluorescence pass through, while retaining the copper radiation which is to be measured.

The presence in the diffraction cell, especially in the windows, of elements capable of emitting a fluorescent radiation which is difficult to absorb must obviously be avoided. It is advisable to build the cell with materials having a low re-emission power, such, for instance, as lead.

Construction of the cells. The delicate parts of the diffraction cells are the windows, which must be thin, of regular thickness, and fairly transparent to X-rays. A number of materials can be used for their construction. For inert gases at room temperatures, cellophane can be used, while mica proves resistant to chemically active

† Private communication.

substances at higher temperatures and pressures. Beryllium (69), aluminium and quartz (110) have also been used; beryllium presents the advantage of having a very low absorption coefficient (17). Table V gives the absorption coefficients μ of cellophane and mica for two different wave-lengths.

TABLE V. After Richter (152)

Radiation	Cellophane	Mica
Cu $K\alpha$, $\lambda = 1\cdot54$ A.	$\mu = 10\cdot0$ cm.$^{-1}$	$\mu = 100\text{--}120$ cm.$^{-1}$
Mo $K\alpha$, $\lambda = 0\cdot71$ A.	$\mu = 1\cdot5$ cm.$^{-1}$	$\mu = 12\text{--}14$ cm.$^{-1}$

Cells for working with hot vapours are least easy to build. Special attention must be paid to the coefficients of thermal expansion of the different materials. For example, the coefficient of mica is smaller than that of steel, and if a mica window is put into place on a steel apparatus while it is at a high temperature, the mica sheet may be crushed and be put out of order after cooling. On the contrary, if put into place when the apparatus is cold, the mica sheet will stretch without damage when the cell is heated (144). Use of materials having identical expansion coefficients, such as glass and mica (86), disposes of this difficulty, and, as is to be expected, a quartz cell having a thin quartz plate as a window (110) resists well at high temperatures.

In the case of gas pressures above or below atmospheric pressure, the cell must be gas-tight. This is essential when vapours susceptible of damaging the photographic emulsion are to be studied under a few atmospheres pressure.

As an example, Plate II and Fig. 78 show the cell built by the writer (144) to study silicochloroform vapour at 100° C. under 4·3 atm. Complete gas-tightness is secured by sealing with 'Apiezon' grease the mica window, 0·05 mm. thick, which is pressed between two stainless steel parts. The grease hardens and becomes a cement in contact with $SiHCl_3$ vapour, so that gas-tightness and mechanical strength are both achieved simultaneously. Such a mica window is completely tight to vacuum and pressure, yielding only to a pressure of 8 atm. The geometrical disposition of the slits and windows, as in the apparatus of van der Grinten and Piérard (86,138),

is such that in the range between 15 and 135° no secondary
radiation from the window E or the absorption apparatus
APC can reach the film, and the absorption in the cylindrical

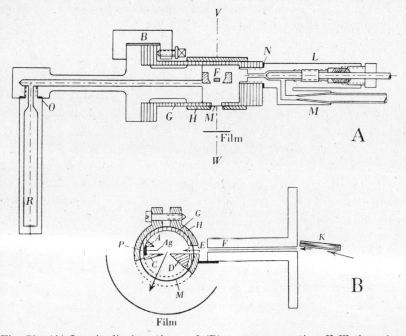

Fig. 78. (A) Longitudinal section and (B) transverse section V-W through a
diffraction cell built for the study of $SiHCl_3$ vapour under pressure.

The primary beam reflected by the crystal K passes through the double slit F,
enters the cell through the mica window E, is scattered by the gas and finally
stopped by the apparatus APC, in which P is a piece of lead and Ag a thin silver
sheet. The prisms C and D limit a slit, 3 mm. wide, through which the scattered
radiation must pass to reach the film. The mica sheet, sealed with 'Apiezon'
grease, is pressed between the tube G and the cylinder H, which are both provided
with suitable apertures to form the entrance and exit windows E and M. The
reservoir R containing liquid silico-chloroform is connected to the diffraction
chamber by a canal through the axis of the apparatus. The tap L being turned off,
the reservoir R is kept at a constant temperature which determines the vapour
pressure inside the cell (e.g. 4·3 atm. at 80° C.), while the rest of the cell is of
course kept at a higher temperature (e.g. 100° C.). The radius of the diffraction
chamber is 1·45 cm. (After Pirenne (144).)

window M is the same at all angles θ. The figure shows that a
double slit F is used for the primary X-ray beam, which gives a
beam divergence only half as great as an ordinary slit. Soller slits,
which are composite slits made up of a number of parallel thin

plates, are sometimes used to obtain a broad X-ray beam of fairly parallel rays [176]. Particulars of other cells will be found in original papers on X-ray scattering by gases.

The heating of the diffraction cells is usually achieved by the use of electrical resistances. In places where the temperature cannot be easily controlled, circulation of steam through a copper tube coiled around the cell is a useful device. The photographic film is kept cool by a stream of water inside the holder.

Plate I shows a microphotometer record of a diffraction photograph of the molecule CCl_4, obtained by using the apparatus shown in Plate II.

THE X-RAY RADIATION

The intensity emitted by X-ray tubes is generally small [89]. The yield of transformation into X-rays of the kinetic energy of the electron beam hitting the anticathode is only of the order of 10^{-3}. As far as mere intensity considerations are concerned, therefore, it is more advantageous [9] to diffract an electron beam by a gas than, first, to use the same electron beam for obtaining X-rays and, secondly, to scatter these X-rays by the gas.

It is impossible to increase indefinitely the intensity emitted by an anti-cathode by using more powerful electron beams. For, in the anticathode, most of the electron energy is converted into heat, which must be dissipated by conduction, and no system of cooling will prevent the melting of the anticathode when a certain critical intensity is exceeded. Rotating anticathodes have to be used to increase the intensity further. This is not the place to give details about the characteristics of all the different X-ray generators.[†] Ott's continuously evacuated tube [134], which has been used by the writer [144], is suited to long exposure times at high intensities. Much more powerful tubes of the rotating anode type have been recently developed by Beck [6] and by Müller and Clay [130]. All these tubes are of the hot filament type. Gas discharge tubes are less powerful, but offer certain advantages: thus, they give less background intensity on the short wave-length side of the $K\alpha$ radiation of the anticathode [9].

† See, for example, the book by Clark [24].

Very soft X-rays are too easily absorbed by matter, while very hard X-rays are so little absorbed that parasitic radiation is very difficult to eliminate. In diffraction experiments, the wave-lengths mostly used are those of the $K\alpha$ line of copper (1·54 A.) and molybdenum (0·71 A.), and sometimes of iron (1·94 A.). Silver radiation (0·56 A.) might probably be used with advantage for working with gases under pressure, on account of its low absorption coefficient. Measurements must refer to radiation which is as nearly monochromatic as possible. For this reason, characteristic lines only are used, since they obviously give the greatest available intensities in very narrow wave-length bands. Irradiation by X-rays does not appear to bring about appreciable chemical changes in gases. This is due in part to the relatively low intensity of the rays (82,89,90).

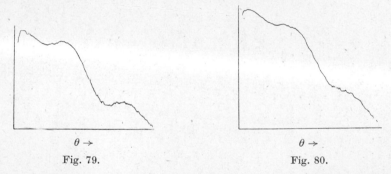

$\theta \rightarrow$ $\theta \rightarrow$

Fig. 79.   Fig. 80.

Fig. 79. Tracing of the microphotometer record of an X-ray diffraction pattern of the molecule $SiHCl_3$ made in 7 hr. 40 min. with rocksalt-reflected $MoK\alpha$ radiation, using the apparatus represented in Fig. 78. The maxima are situated at about $\theta = 25°$ and $\theta = 41°$, respectively. (After Pirenne(145).)

Fig. 80. Tracing of the microphotometer record of an X-ray diffraction photograph made in 15 min. using $MoK\alpha$ radiation filtered through a zirconium foil, using the same apparatus as in Fig. 79. (After Pirenne(145).)

Fig. 79 shows the microphotometer record of a diffraction photograph of $SiHCl_3$ made by using monochromatic, crystal-reflected X-rays. Fig. 80 shows the record of a photograph of the same gas made under the same conditions except for the fact that imperfectly monochromatic radiation, namely, filtered radiation from an Ott tube, was used. Comparison of these figures proves that the latter radiation is unsuitable for quantitative intensity measurements, for in the second figure no trace is left of the second maximum and minimum in the first, except an inflexion in the curve. Van der Grinten[85], studying CCl_4, also found that filtered radiation is inadequate, while the diffraction of crystal-reflected X-rays[86] gives a scattering curve in remarkable agreement with theory.[†]

Filters. If the primary radiation contains an appreciable amount of hard general radiation, no complete monochromatization can be achieved by using selective filters only[160,157,127]. In the case of a favourable spectral distribution, as may be given by a gas discharge tube, relatively pure radiation may be obtained. This must be the reason why the first CCl_4 photographs obtained by Bewilogua[9] using this technique show maxima which are more prominent than those of more recent photographs made using the filtered radiation of an Ott tube. For preliminary investigations, the filtered radiation of an ion tube, or even of an electron tube, may be advantageously used.[‡] Table VI gives characteristics of filters used for three different radiations, according to Bewilogua[9].

TABLE VI.   After Bewilogua[9]

Anticathode	Wave-length of the $K\alpha$ line in A.	Filter	Per cent. absorption	
			$K\alpha$	$K\beta$
Copper	1·54	10μ nickel foil	35	93
Molybdenum	0·71	70μ zirconium foil	55	94
Iron	1·94	11 mg./cm.^{2} MnO_2 powder	30	95

In the case of Debye-Scherrer powder photographs, imperfectly monochromatic radiation can often be used, because the rings which correspond to the characteristic lines of the primary radiation are very sharp and remain visible on the diffuse background. In

---

[†] Similar conclusions have been reached in the study of X-ray diffraction by liquids [84].

[‡] The fact that the same values of the interatomic distances have been obtained for CCl_4 using crystal-reflected and filtered radiation [140] does not prove that the latter is generally adequate. For, in the case of CCl_4, the Cl-Cl distances have a predominant influence in the diffraction formula (see Chapter x) so that the *positions* of the maxima and minima of intensity are the determining factors, and these positions may be unaffected by the use of filtered radiation. But in other cases the intensities are a decisive factor [144].

diffraction by gases or liquids, monochromatic radiation is necessary (127, 84), but on the other hand, slits much broader than those
which are used in the study of crystals may be used, for the very
reason that the pattern is already naturally diffuse. This is an important advantage in experiments made with crystal-reflected X-rays.

Crystal monochromators. Crystal reflexion gives the purest
X-ray radiation but may cut down the intensity considerably, by
a factor 10 or more, this leading to long times of exposure. It is
therefore fortunate that broad slits can be used in the diffraction by
gases. The broad slit can take in the whole of the radiation emitted
in one direction by the anticathode of the X-ray tube. It is not
necessary as in crystal analysis to work with a point source. On the
other hand, these conditions make it unlikely that the method of
Fankuchen (72, 73) will be able to increase the total X-ray energy
available for gas diffraction. This method uses the reflexion from the
surface of a crystal cut at an angle in order to transform a broad
X-ray beam into a narrower but more intense beam. Such narrow
beams, however, may prove useful in the study of the scattering at
very small θ angles.

In the case of powder diagrams and of X-ray spectroscopy, crystals
which have been plastically curved, or which have been ground, or
which have been both ground and curved, are used for focusing
X-rays. These devices reunite the rays of a divergent beam originating from a small source (117, 88, 16). Unfortunately, they seem difficult to adapt with advantage to the measurement of diffraction by
gases.

The problem of obtaining the best intensity yield from a crystal
monochromator is complicated. Crystal and cell evidently must
be brought as close as possible to the anticathode. A crystal with a
high 'integrated reflexion' intensity for the wave-length used must
be chosen. This reflected intensity depends upon the treatment to
which the crystal has previously been submitted. An extensive
comparison of rock-salt and calcite has been made from these
points of view by Wagner and Kulenkampff (167). The voltage on the
X-ray generator must be chosen in such a way that the intensity
of the spectral line to be used is high (101), without the intensity
of the second-order reflexion becoming troublesome. Radiation

reflected from a crystal is partially polarized, so that in formulae such as (65) a special polarization factor (86) has to be used instead of the factor $\frac{1}{2}(1 + \cos^2 \theta)$.

Balanced filters. Ross has invented a method by which the intensity corresponding to a very narrow range of wave-lengths is determined by taking the difference between two measurements, in neither of which is monochromatic radiation actually used. The principle of Ross's 'balanced filters' method is summarized as follows by its author (153):

'This method consists in using two adjacent elements (silver-cadmium, palladium-silver, platinum-gold, etc.) in the path of the X-ray beam. The thicknesses of the two foils are so adjusted that the transmission curves of the two coincide except between their K

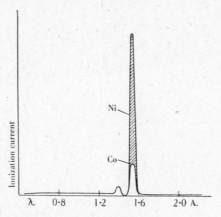

Fig. 81. Transmission of the X-ray spectrum of a copper anticathode through balanced filters of nickel and cobalt. (After Herzog (100).)

discontinuities. These balanced foils are mounted on a carrier in front of the window of an ionization chamber so that either foil may be moved into exact position in front of the window at will. The increase in ionization current, when the metal of higher atomic number is substituted for the one of lower atomic number, is due to the band of radiation between their K absorption limits.'

A strong characteristic line of the anticathode spectrum can be isolated by this method. Fig. 81, after Herzog, shows the transmission curves of the radiation emitted by a copper anticathode for

balanced filters of nickel and cobalt. The shaded area corresponds
to the difference of transmission of the two filters, and therefore to
the radiation band to which the measurements will refer; its half-
intensity width is 0·06 A. The superiority of this method over the
use of a nickel filter alone is immediately seen on the figure: all
general radiation and the $K\beta$ line are eliminated.

The difficulties of the method reside in the preparation of the
filters. It has been employed successfully by Wollan[176] using
molybdenum radiation to measure the scattering functions of
various gases, and by Herzog[100] using copper radiation for the
absolute determination of the intensity scattered by argon. Wollan[179] has also developed a triple system of balanced filters, for
molybdenum radiation, which enabled him to measure separately
the coherent, incoherent, and total intensities scattered by oxygen,
nitrogen and argon, at a particular angle. More recently, Hoffmann[102] has determined separately the coherent and incoherent
scattering functions of C_2H_2 and CO_2, using balanced filters and
photographic recording. This is especially interesting in view of the
fact that balanced filters had previously been considered unsuitable
for monochromatic measurements, by the photographic method, of
the scattering functions of polyatomic gases. It appears now that
the latter problem is relatively simple and could be solved, for
example, by making a pair of photographs under exactly the same
experimental conditions except for the placing of different filters
in the path of the incident beam. Such a method would be especially
valuable since, using filtered radiation, photographs can be made
in less than 1 hr., as mentioned in connexion with Fig. 80.

RECORDING OF SCATTERED INTENSITIES

Ionization chambers. Quantitative measurements of X-ray
intensities are best carried out using ionization chambers. The
radiation to be measured is absorbed as completely as possible in a
chamber filled with gas. The whole X-ray energy is thus used up to
ionize the gas in the chamber. The chamber being built as an electric
condenser, the ions formed are brought to the electrodes by the
electric field. The ionization current so produced has an intensity

which serves as a measure of the absorbed X-ray intensities. Under certain conditions a direct proportionality exists between the two.

For low X-ray intensities, the ionization current is very weak, and the limitations of the method are those of the measurement of these small currents. Ionization chambers were used in the early experiments on rare gases. Wollan[176] used a large diffraction cell with Soller slits S_1 and S_2, and a Compton electrometer capable of measuring currents of 5×10^{-15} amp. (Fig. 82). Herzog[100] used a special amplifying device with a triode tube, and measured currents of 10^{-17} amp. These sensitivities, however, still remain too low for the measurement of the scattering of crystal-reflected radiation by gases.

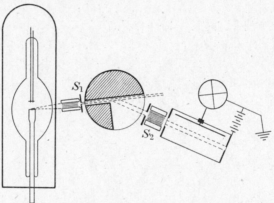

Fig. 82. (After Wollan[176].)

Lu[120] has measured the scattering function of the polyatomic gases Cl_2, CO_2, N_2O, H_2S, CCl_4, and $CHCl_3$ using an ionization chamber.

The ionometric method has the advantage of giving directly a quantitative measure of the intensity. The chamber can also be filled with a gas absorbing selectively the radiation to be measured, while allowing parasitic radiation to pass through, as mentioned above in connexion with fluorescent radiation. On the other hand, its sensitivity is limited, and the measurement of scattering functions must be made point by point, which necessitates a very constant source of X-rays.

Geiger-Müller counters. Counters for X-ray photons can be used in much the same way as ionization chambers, and they are more sensitive. The scattering function of CCl_4 vapour for filtered molybdenum radiation has been measured in this way by van der Grinten and Brasseur (87) with good accuracy. Eisenstein and Gingrich (68) have measured the scattering by liquids using the same method. Ohlin (132) has also reported results of X-ray intensity recordings with Geiger-Müller counters.

Photographic recording of the intensity. The photographic method is the most widely used in the study of X-ray scattering by polyatomic molecules. Extremely weak intensities can be recorded by the photographic films, provided the exposures be sufficiently long, because the effect of the radiation on the film is cumulative.[†]

The photographic recording is done simultaneously at all scattering angles. Thus the X-ray source does not need to be constant and the exposures may be interrupted. Special films are used for X-ray work. Nevertheless their sensitivity may not be very high, largely because the emulsion does not absorb enough of the radiation. For this reason, it may sometimes be advisable to use two superposed films, especially for radiation of short wave-length. New, more sensitive, types of film, however, are being developed (80). Intensifying screens placed behind the film may increase the blackening considerably, especially in the case of hard radiation. Some newly devised screens are very active, and are effective even for radiation as soft as copper radiation (116), but their use appears to be unpractical when true intensity measurements are necessary (80), which reduces considerably their usefulness in X-ray diffraction by gases. In general, the arrangement is such that the photographic emulsion is struck by the radiation falling normally on its surface. This, however, is not necessary, as an appropriate correction can be made if the rays strike the film obliquely (29).

From the blackening of the film, exact (relative) intensities must be derived. This is best done using intensity marks obtained with a rotating sector. Both scattering pattern and intensity marks are measured with a microphotometer and the relative intensities are directly deduced from the microphotometer record. In this way,

---

† DuMond and Kirkpatrick (64) have been able to obtain a photograph of the Compton spectrum emitted by helium gas after 2059 hr. of exposure.

the blackening law of the film is determined in each experiment. Conditions as identical as possible are of course employed for the treatment of the photographs and of the intensity marks. The use of a rotating sector is possible because in Schwartzschild's law, $S = f(It^p)$ (S blackening, I intensity, t time), the exponent p is very nearly unity in the case of X-rays. On this subject, details, notably on the non-dependence of the blackening law upon the wave-length, have been given by Bewilogua [9]. It must be noted that this applies to photographs made without using intensifying screens.

CALCULATIONS AND CORRECTIONS

Since Fourier analysis is not suitable for determining the structure of free molecules from X-ray diffraction data, the ordinary trial-and-error method must be used. A plausible model of the molecule is assumed and the corresponding scattering function is calculated using formula (65), or formula (84) if the temperature effect is to be taken into account. Now, this function cannot be compared directly with the experimental intensity curve. Corrections must be made to take into account the dependence upon the scattering angle of the size of the effective scattering volume [86], of the distance between the scattering volume and the film [7], of the angle which the diffraction slit subtends at the film [86], and of the thickness of absorbing matter traversed in the gas and in the windows [9]. A further correction is sometimes needed because the absorption of the incoherent scattering is different from the absorption of the coherent scattering [113]. It seems better to apply these corrections to the theoretical curve rather than to apply them in reverse to the experimental curve. This makes it easier to estimate the precision attained. The calculation of the theoretical curves must be made accurately, point by point, and is often laborious. Graphical interpolation, however, can do much in the way of shortening the calculations. Each periodic term may be drawn separately and fewer points are then needed for the interpolations. Again, interpolation between curves relating to slightly dissimilar structures may give useful approximations at the preliminary stages of comparison.

COMPARISON WITH ELECTRON DIFFRACTION

Although based on the same principle, X-ray and electron diffraction by gases are very dissimilar in practice. The times of exposure are much longer for X-ray than for electrons, but, as has been said above, they are on the way to being reduced to quite convenient lengths. For instance the use of balanced filters offers the possibility of making, in less than one hour, photographs giving monochromatic measurements. Electron diffraction has the advantage that the apparatus can be used with little change for substances having widely different physico-chemical properties. Moreover, it can be adapted to the study of vapours at temperatures of the order of $1000°$ C., as is necessary for such molecules as S_2 (124) and the alkali halide molecules (125). On the other hand, quantitative intensity measurements are more easily obtained using X-rays than using electrons. All processes occurring in X-ray diffraction cells can be brought well under control and taken into account in the calculations. Again, the X-ray wave-lengths used are natural constants. These are considerations of experimental interest. The theoretical scope of two methods of diffraction by gases has been fully discussed in Chapter x.

CHAPTER XIII

MOLECULES STUDIED BY X-RAY DIFFRACTION

THE main problems of molecular structure which can be studied by the method of X-ray diffraction by gases have already been reviewed in this monograph. A list of the polyatomic molecules for which the X-ray scattering functions have been determined is given below. These measurements have been made for widely different purposes.

Although the accurate location of the atom centres was not always the aim of the investigation—it being even impossible in some cases, such as that of the CH_4 molecule—a number of important stereochemical problems have been studied with success by X-ray diffraction. For instance, among the very first molecules to be studied were the two 1.2-dichloroethylenes: it was found that the *trans* form has an appreciably larger Cl-Cl distance than the *cis* form, as was expected. Again, it has been shown in C_6H_6, and especially well in C_6Cl_6, that the hexagonal ring is planar.

The example of CCl_4 shows that a high accuracy is attainable in the X-ray measurement of interatomic distances. The CCl_4 molecule has become a 'standard' molecule for diffraction experiments. The numerous investigations, both by X-ray and electron diffraction, to which it has been submitted have been reviewed by Debye [50].

From the first investigation of the series CCl_4, $CHCl_3$ and CH_2Cl_2, it had been concluded that the Cl-Cl distance is larger in this series when the number of Cl atoms in the molecule is smaller. Recent measurements confirm this result for CCl_4 and $CHCl_3$, the Cl-Cl distance being 3·5 % larger in the latter molecule. In an X-ray investigation of $SiHCl_3$, the valency angle itself was measured with precision and shown to be definitely larger than the regular tetrahedral angle (Cl-Si-Cl = $111·5° \pm 1°$). More experimental work is needed on such molecules, the structure of which is interesting because it gives information about the attraction and repulsion forces acting between atoms. The reader is referred to the writer's discussion of this subject [144].

Table VII gives references to the papers dealing with the X-ray scattering functions of gas molecules and with their geometrical structures as determined by the X-ray method. Except in a few cases, the interatomic distances values are not reproduced, because these data would be of little interest if unaccompanied in each case by thorough discussion of the accuracy of the measurements and comparison with the results of other methods of structure determination. Again it must be borne in mind that the determination of interatomic distances was by no means the only aim of many X-ray investigations. The distances found, especially in older investigations, may in some cases suffer from error without the investigation losing its value for the specific problem it was designed to solve.

X-ray diffraction by gases until now has remained mostly a physicist's field of investigation. The main types of problem have been solved in such a way as to place the method on a sound theoretical and experimental basis. And if no extensive study of series of molecules has as yet been undertaken—as has been done using electron diffraction—this neglect may in part be due to misunderstandings which have sometimes arisen about the possibilities of the X ray diffraction method.

TABLE VII. *Molecules studied by X-ray diffraction*

Molecule		References (given in chronological order) and dimensions
H_2		176
H_2O		79, 162
NH_3		79, 162
CH_4		152, 162
H_2S		120
N_2		44, 175, 79
O_2		175, 79
Cl_2		151, 120, 152
C_2H_2		102
CO_2		44, 79, 120, 102
CS_2		44, 79
N_2O		120
$N(CH_3)_3$		152
CCl_4		39, 40, 41, 45, 44, 9, 120, 86, 58, 140, 87, 50 (Cl-Cl = $2 \cdot 86 \pm 0 \cdot 01$ A.)
$CHCl_3$		39, 40, 41, 45, 9, 120, 139 (Cl-Cl = $2 \cdot 96$ A.)
CH_2Cl_2		39, 40, 41, 45, 9, 144
CH_3Cl		39, 40, 45, 9, 144
$SiCl_4$		110, 144
$SiHCl_3$		143, 144, 145 (Cl-Cl = $3 \cdot 27 \pm 0 \cdot 03$ A.; Si-Cl = $1 \cdot 98 \pm 0 \cdot 02$ A.; angle Cl-Si-Cl = $111\frac{1}{2}° \pm 1°$)
$CHCl_2$—CH_3		42, 67
CH_2Cl—CH_2Cl		42, 67
CH_2Cl—$CHCl$—CH_3		7
CH_2Cl—CH_2—CH_2Cl		7
CH_2Cl—CH_2—CH_2—CH_2—CH_2Cl		7
$CHCl$=$CHCl$	*cis*	42, 44, 67
$CHCl$=$CHCl$	*trans*	42, 44, 67
CH_3OH		148
CH_3—CH_2OH		148
CH_3—CH_2—CH_2OH		148
CH_3—CH_2—CH_2—CH_2OH		148
$(CH_3)_2CHOH$		148
$(CH_3)_3COH$		148
C_6H_6		113, 155, 162
C_6H_5Cl		142, 155
C_6H_5Br		155
C_6H_5I		155
$C_6H_4Cl_2$	*ortho*	141, 142, 155
$C_6H_4Cl_2$	*meta*	141, 155
$C_6H_4Cl_2$	*para*	141, 142, 155
$C_6H_4Br_2$	*ortho*	155
$C_6H_4Br_2$	*para*	155
$C_6H_3Cl_3$	1.2.4	155
C_6Cl_6		113

TABLE VIII. *Atomic scattering factors f*

(After James and Brindley (109). See Chapter I, page 19)

$\frac{\sin\frac{1}{2}\theta}{\lambda}$, λ in Å.	0	0·1	0·2	0·3	0·4	0·5	0·6	0·7	0·8	0·9	1·0	1·1	Remarks
H	1·0	0·81	0·48	0·25	0·13	0·07	0·04	0·03	0·02	0·01	0·00	0·00	W
He	2·0	1·88	1·46	1·05	0·75	0·52	0·35	0·24	0·18	0·14	0·11	0·09	H
Li$^+$	2·0	1·96	1·8	1·5	1·3	1·0	0·8	0·6	0·5	0·4	0·3	0·3	H
Li (neut.)	3·0	2·2	1·8	1·5	1·3	1·0	0·8	0·6	0·5	0·4	0·3	0·3	H
Be^{+2}	2·0	2·0	1·9	1·7	1·6	1·4	1·2	1·0	0·9	0·7	0·6	0·5	I
Be (neut.)	4·0	2·9	1·9	1·7	1·6	1·4	1·2	1·0	0·9	0·7	0·6	0·5	I
B^{+3}	2·0	2·0	1·9	1·8	1·7	1·6	1·4	1·3	1·2	1·0	0·9	0·7	I
B (neut.)	5·0	3·5	2·4	1·9	1·7	1·5	1·4	1·2	1·2	1·0	0·9	0·7	I
C	6·0	4·6	3·0	2·2	1·9	1·7	1·6	1·4	1·3	1·2	1·0	0·9	I
N^{+5}	2·0	2·0	2·0	1·9	1·9	1·8	1·7	1·6	1·5	1·4	1·3	1·16	I
N^{+3}	4·0	3·7	3·0	2·4	2·0	1·8	1·65	1·55	1·5	1·4	1·3	1·15	I
N (neut.)	7·0	5·8	4·2	3·0	2·3	1·9	1·65	1·55	1·5	1·4	1·3	1·15	I
O (neut.)	8·0	7·1	5·3	3·9	2·9	2·2	1·8	1·6	1·5	1·4	1·35	1·25	H
O^{-2}	10·0	8·0	5·5	3·8	2·7	2·1	1·8	1·5	1·5	1·4	1·35	1·25	I+H
F$^-$	10·0	8·7	6·7	4·8	3·5	2·8	2·2	1·9	1·7	1·55	1·5	1·35	H
F (neut.)	9·0	7·8	6·2	4·45	3·35	2·65	2·15	1·9	1·7	1·6	1·5	1·35	H
Ne	10·0	9·3	7·5	5·8	4·4	3·4	2·65	2·2	1·9	1·65	1·55	1·5	I
Na$^+$	10·0	9·5	8·2	6·7	5·25	4·05	3·2	2·65	2·25	1·95	1·75	1·6	H
Na	11·0	9·65	8·2	6·7	5·25	4·05	3·2	2·65	2·25	1·95	1·75	1·6	H
Mg^{+2}	10·0	9·75	8·6	7·25	5·05	4·8	3·85	3·15	2·55	2·2	2·0	1·8	I
Mg	12·0	10·5	8·6	7·22	5·05	4·8	3·85	3·15	2·55	2·2	2·0	1·8	I
Al^{+3}	10·0	9·7	8·9	7·8	6·65	5·5	4·45	3·65	3·1	2·65	2·3	2·0	H
Al^{+2}	11·0	10·3	9·0	7·75	6·6	5·5	4·5	3·7	3·1	2·65	2·3	2·0	H
Al$^+$	12·0	10·9	9·0	7·75	6·6	5·5	4·5	3·7	3·1	2·65	2·3	2·0	H
Al	13·0	11·0	8·95	7·75	6·6	5·5	4·5	3·7	3·1	2·65	2·3	2·0	H+I
Si^{+4}	10·0	9·75	9·15	8·25	7·15	6·05	5·05	4·2	3·4	2·95	2·6	2·3	H
Si^{+2}	12·0	11·1	9·55	8·2	7·15	6·05	5·05	4·2	3·4	2·95	2·6	2·3	H+I
Si	14·0	11·35	9·4	8·2	7·15	6·1	5·1	4·2	3·4	2·95	2·6	2·3	H+I
P^{+5}	10·0	9·8	9·25	8·45	7·5	6·55	5·65	4·8	4·05	3·4	3·0	2·6	I
P (neut.)	15·0	12·4	10·0	8·45	7·45	6·5	5·65	4·8	4·05	3·4	3·0	2·6	I
P^{-3}	18·0	12·7	9·8	8·4	7·45	6·5	5·65	4·85	4·05	3·4	3·0	2·6	I
S (neut.)	16·0	13·6	10·7	8·95	7·85	6·85	6·0	5·25	4·5	3·9	3·35	2·9	I
S^{+6}	10·0	9·85	9·4	8·7	7·85	6·85	6·05	5·25	4·5	3·9	3·35	2·9	I
S^{-2}	18·0	14·3	10·7	8·9	7·85	6·85	6·0	5·25	4·5	3·9	3·35	2·9	I
Cl	17·0	14·6	11·3	9·25	8·05	7·25	6·5	5·75	5·05	4·4	3·85	3·35	H+I
Cl$^-$	18·0	15·2	11·5	9·3	8·05	7·25	6·5	5·75	5·05	4·4	3·85	3·35	H
A	18·0	15·9	12·6	10·4	8·7	7·8	7·0	6·2	5·4	4·7	4·1	3·6	I
K$^+$	18·0	16·5	13·3	10·8	8·85	7·75	7·05	6·44	5·9	5·3	4·8	4·2	H
Ca^{+2}	18·0	16·8	14·0	11·5	9·3	8·1	7·35	6·7	6·2	5·7	5·1	4·6	I
Sc^{+3}	18·0	16·7	14·0	11·4	9·4	8·3	7·6	6·9	6·4	5·8	5·35	4·75	I
Ti^{+4}	18·0	17·0	14·4	11·9	9·9	8·5	7·85	7·3	6·7	6·15	5·65	5·05	I
Ti^{+2}	20·0	18·7	15·5	12·5	10·1	8·5	7·8	7·25	6·7	6·15	5·65	5·05	I
Cu$^+$	28·0	27·0	24·0	20·7	17·3	14·0	11·3	9·4	8·0	7·3	7·0	6·7	I
Cu$^+$	28·0	26·3	23·0	19·2	15·8	13·0	11·2	9·7	8·4	7·4	6·7	6·5	H(approx.)
Cu	29·0	25·8	21·4	17·8	15·2	13·3	11·7	10·2	9·1	8·1	7·3	6·7	T
Rb$^+$	36·0	33·6	28·7	24·6	21·4	18·9	16·7	14·6	12·8	11·2	9·9	8·9	H
Rb	37·0	33·4	28·2	23·6	20·4	17·9	15·9	14·0	12·4	11·2	10·2	9·9	T

I = calculated by method of interpolation.
H = calculated from Hartree distribution.
T = calculated from Thomas model.
W = calculated from hydrogen wave-function (ground state).

BIBLIOGRAPHY

(*Titles are given when they are especially informative in connexion with the subject-matter of the present book. Review articles and books are marked with an asterisk.*)

(1) ALLISON, S.K. and JESSE, W.P. (1936). Experiments on the variation of the atomic structure factor of potassium with X-ray wavelength. *Phys. Rev.* **49**, 483–94.

(2) BARRETT, C.S. (1928). The scattering of X-rays from gases. *Phys. Rev.* **32**, 22–9.

(3) BAUER, S.H. (1943). *Phys. Rev.* **64**, 316.

(4) BEACH, J.Y. and PALMER, K.J. (1938). *J. Chem. Phys.* **6**, 639–44.

(5) BEACH, J.Y. and TURKEVITCH, A. (1939). *J. Amer. Chem. Soc.* **61**, 303–8.

(6) BECK, J. (1939). *Phys. Z.* **40**, 474–83.

(7) BERGER, H. (1937). Interferometrische Messungen an halogensubstituirten Paraffinen. *Phys. Z.* **38**, 370–9.

(8) BEWILOGUA, L. (1931). Über die Genauigkeit von Interferenzmessungen in der Molekel mit Röntgen- und Kathodenstrahlen. *Phys. Z.* **32**, 114–17.

(9) BEWILOGUA, L. (1931). Interferometrische Messungen an einzelnen Molekeln der Chlor-Substitutionsprodukte des Methan. *Phys. Z.* **32**, 265–82.

(10) BEWILOGUA, L. (1931). Über die inkohärente Streuung der Röntgenstrahlen. *Phys. Z.* **32**, 740–4.

(11) BEWILOGUA, L. (1932). Über die Streuung von Röntgen- und Kathodenstrahlen an freien Molekülen. *Phys. Z.* **33**, 688–92.

(12) BLACKMAN, M. (1939). On the intensities of electron diffraction rings. *Proc. Roy. Soc.* A, **173**, 68–82.

(13) BOHR, N. (1913). *Phil. Mag.* **26**, 489–502.

(14) BORN, M. and SARGINSON, K. (1941). The effect of thermal vibrations on the scattering of X-rays. *Proc. Roy. Soc.* A, **179**, 68–93.

*(15) BORN, M. (1943). Theoretical investigations on the relation between crystal dynamics and X-ray scattering. *Rep. Progr. Phys.* **9**, 294–333.

(16) BOZORTH, R.M. and HAWORTH, F.E. (1938). *Phys. Rev.* **53**, 538–44.

(17) BRACKNEY, H. and ATLEE, Z.J. (1943). *Rev. Sci. Instrum.* **14**, 59–63.

*(18) BRAGG, SIR W.H. and BRAGG, W.L. (1933). *The Crystalline State.* Vol. 1. *A General Survey*, by W.L. BRAGG. London.

(19) BRAY, E.E. and GINGRICH, N.S. (1943). *J. Chem. Phys.* **11**, 351–4.

(20) BREIT, G. (1926). A correspondence principle in the Compton effect. *Phys. Rev.* **27**, 362–72.

(21) BRILL, R., GRIMM, H.G., HERMANN, C. and PETERS, CL. (1939). *Ann. Phys., Lpz.*, [5], **34**, 393–445.

*(22) BROCKWAY, L.O. (1936). Electron diffraction by gas molecules. *Rev. Mod. Phys.* **8**, 231–66.

(23) CAMPBELL, J.A. and HILDEBRAND, J.H. (1943). *J. Chem. Phys.* **11**, 330–3.

*(24) CLARK, G.L. (1940). *Applied X-rays.* New York and London.

(25) COMPTON, A.H. (1923). A quantum theory of the scattering of X-rays by light elements. *Phys. Rev.* **21**, 483–502.

(26) COMPTON, A.H. (1923). The spectrum of scattered X-rays. *Phys. Rev.* **22**, 409–13.

(27) COMPTON, A.H. (1930). The determination of electron distributions from measurements of scattered X-rays. *Phys. Rev.* **35**, 925–38.

*(28) COMPTON, A.H. and ALLISON, S.K. (1935). *X-rays in Theory and Experiment.* Second edition of *X-rays and Electrons*, by A.H. COMPTON. New York and London.

(29) COX, E.G. and SHAW, W.F.B. (1930). *Proc. Roy. Soc.* A, **127**, 71–88.

(30) DEBYE, P. (1913). *Verh. dtsch. phys. Ges.* **15**, 678–89, 738–52, 857–75.

(31) DEBYE, P. (1914). Interferenz von Röntgenstrahlen und Wärmebewegung. *Ann. Phys.*, *Lpz.*, **43**, 49–95.

(32) DEBYE, P. (1915). Zerstreuung von Röntgenstrahlen. *Ann. Phys.*, *Lpz.*, **46**, 809–23.

(33) DEBYE, P. and SCHERRER, P. (1916). *Ges. Wiss. Göttingen*, pp. 1–15.

(34) DEBYE, P. and SCHERRER, P. (1916). *Ges. Wiss. Göttingen*, pp. 16–26.

(35) DEBYE, P. and SCHERRER, P. (1916). Interferenzen an regellos orientierten Teilchen im Röntgenlicht. *Phys. Z.* **17**, 277–83.

(36) DEBYE, P. (1923). Zerstreuung von Röntgenstrahlen und Quantentheorie. *Phys. Z.* **24**, 161–6.

(37) DEBYE, P. (1925). Note on the scattering of X-rays. *J. Math. Phys.* **4**, 133–47.

(38) DEBYE, P. (1927). Über die Zerstreuung von Röntgenstrahlen an amorphen Körpern. *Phys. Z.* **28**, 135–41.

(39) DEBYE, P., BEWILOGUA, L. and EHRHARDT, F. (1929). Interferometrische Messungen am Molekül. *Ber. sächs. Ges.* (*Akad.*) *Wiss.* **81**, 29–37.

(40) DEBYE, P., BEWILOGUA, L. and EHRHARDT, F. (1929). Zerstreuung von Röntgenstrahlen an einzelnen Molekeln (vorläufige Mitteilung). *Phys. Z.* **30**, 84–7.

(41) DEBYE, P. (1929). Interferometrische Messungen am Molekül. *Phys. Z.* **30**, 524–5.

(42) DEBYE, P. (1930). Röntgeninterferenzen an isomeren Molekülen (nach Versüchen mit L. BEWILOGUA und F. EHRHARDT). *Phys. Z.* **31**, 142.

(43) DEBYE, P. (1930). Röntgenzerstreuung an Flüssigkeiten und Gasen. *Phys. Z.* **31**, 348–50.

(44) DEBYE, P. (1930). Röntgeninterferenzen und Atomgrösse. *Phys. Z.* **31**, 419–28.

(45) DEBYE, P. (1930). Interferometrische Bestimmung der Struktur von Einzelmolekülen. *Z. Elektrochem.* **36**, 612–15.

*(46) DEBYE, P. and MENKE, H. (1931). Untersuchung der molekülaren Ordnung in Flüssigkeiten mit Röntgenstrahlung. *Ergebn. tech. Röntgenk.* **2**, 1–22.

*(47) DEBYE, P. (1933). Streuung von Röntgen- und Kathodenstrahlen. *Ergebn. tech. Röntgenk.* **3**, 11–25.

*(48) DEBYE, P. (1933). *Struktur der Materie*, Vier Vorträge. Leipzig.

(49) DEBYE, P. (1937). Die Untersuchung der freien Elektronen in Metallen mit Hilfe von Röntgenstrahlen. *Phys. Z.* **38**, 161–5.

*(50) DEBYE, P. (1937). *Methoden zur Bestimmung der elektrischen und geometrischen Struktur von Molekülen*. Nobel Lecture, Stockholm.

(51) DEBYE, P. and PIRENNE, M.H. (1938). Über die Fourieranalyse von interferometrischen Messungen an freien Molekülen. *Ann. Phys., Lpz.*, **33**, 617–29.

(52) DEBYE, P. (1939). Das Sektorverfahren bei der Aufnahme von Elektroneninterferenzen. *Phys. Z.* **40**, 507–8.

(53) DEBYE, P. (1939). Untersuchung eines neuen Vorschlags zur Fourier-Analyse von Elektronenaufnahmen. *Phys. Z.* **40**, 573–77.

*(54) DEBYE, P. (1939). Die quasikristalline Struktur von Flüssigkeiten. *Z. Elektroch.* **45**, 174–80.

(55) DEBYE, P. (1941). Influence of intramolecular atomic motion on electron diffraction diagrams. *J. Chem. Phys.* **9**, 55–60.

(56) DEBYE, P.P. (1939). Ein neues Aufnahmeverfahren von Elektroneninterferenzen an einzelnen Molekülen. *Phys. Z.* **40**, 66.

(57) DEBYE, P.P. (1939). Elektroneninterferenzen an leichten Molekülen nach dem Sektorverfahren. *Phys. Z.* **40**, 404–6.

(58) DEGARD, C., PIÉRARD, J. and VAN DER GRINTEN, W. (1935). Diffraction of X-rays and electrons by carbon tetrachloride vapour. *Nature, Lond.*, **136**, 142–3.

(59) DEGARD, C. and VAN DER GRINTEN, W. (1935). Étude de la structure des molécules gazeuses au moyen des rayons électroniques. *IIe Congrès National des Sciences*, pp. 653–67. Bruxelles.

(60) DIRAC, P.A.M. (1926). Relativity quantum mechanics with an application to Compton scattering. *Proc. Roy. Soc.* A, **111**, 405–23.

(61) DIRAC, P.A.M. (1928). The quantum theory of the electron. *Proc. Roy. Soc.* A, **117**, 610–24.

(62) DIRAC, P.A.M. (1930). Note on exchange phenomena in the Thomas atom. *Proc. Camb. Phil. Soc.* **26**, 376–85.

*(63) DuMOND, J.W.M. (1933). The linear momenta of electrons in atoms and in solid bodies as revealed by X-ray scattering. *Rev. Mod. Phys.* **5**, 1–33.

(64) DuMOND, J.W.M. and KIRKPATRICK, H.A. (1937). *Phys. Rev.* **52**, 419–36.

*(65) EHRENBERG, W. and SCHÄFER, K. (1932). Bericht über Atomfaktoren. *Phys. Z.* **33**, 97–122.

EHRENBERG, W. and SCHÄFER, K. (1932). Nachtrag zu dem Bericht über Atomfaktoren. *Phys. Z.* **33**, 575–6.

(66) EHRENFEST, P. (1915). Über Interferenzerscheinungen, die zu erwarten sind, wenn Röntgenstrahlen durch ein zweiatomiges Gas gehen. *Proc. K. Akad. Wet. Amst.* **23**, 1132.

(67) EHRHARDT, F. (1932). Röntgeninterferenzen an Molekülen mit zwei Kohlenstoffatomen. *Phys. Z.* **33**, 605–14.

(68) EISENSTEIN, A. and GINGRICH, N.S. (1941). *Rev. Sci. Instrum.* **12**, 582–86.

(69) EISENSTEIN, A. and GINGRICH, N.S. (1942). The diffraction of X-rays by argon in the liquid, vapor and critical regions. *Phys. Rev.* **62**, 261–70.

(70) EISENSTEIN, A. (1943). *Phys. Rev.* **63**, 305–8.

(71) EWALD, P.P. and HÖNL, H. (1936). Die Röntgeninterferenzen an Diamant als wellenmechanisches Problem. *Ann. Phys., Lpz.*, **25**, 281–308; **26**, 673–96.

(72) FANKUCHEN, I. (1937). *Nature, Lond.*, **139**, 193–4.

(73) FANKUCHEN, I. (1938). *Phys. Rev.* **53**, 910.

(74) FERMI, E. (1926). Zur Quantelung des idealen einatomigen Gases. *Z. Phys.* **36**, 902–12.

(75) FERMI, E. (1928). Eine statistische Methode zur Bestimmung einiger Eigenschaften des Atoms und ihre Anwendung auf die Theorie des periodischen Systems der Elemente. *Z. Phys.* **48**, 73–9.

(76) FOCK, V. (1930). Näherungsmethode zur Lösung des quantenmechanischen Mehrkörperproblems. *Z. Phys.* **61**, 126–48.

*(77) FRENKEL, J. (1932). *Wave-Mechanics. Elementary Theory.* Oxford.

(78) FRIEDRICH, W., KNIPPING, P. and LAUE, M. (1912). Interferenz-Erscheinungen bei Röntgenstrahlen. *Münch. Akad. Wiss.* pp. 303–22.

(79) GAJEWSKI, H. (1932). Die Zerstreuung von Röntgenstrahlen an einfachen Gasen (N_2, O_2, CO_2, CS_2, NH_3, H_2O). *Phys. Z.* **33**, 122–31.

(80) GAMERSTFELDER, C. and GINGRICH, N.S. (1938). *Rev. Sci. Instrum.* **9**, 154–9.

*(81) GINGRICH, N.S. (1943). Diffraction of X-rays by liquid elements. *Rev. Mod. Phys.* **15**, 90–110.

(82) GLOCKER, K. (1928). Über die Gesetzmässigkeiten der physikalischen und chemischen Wirkung der Röntgenstrahlen. *Z. tech. Phys.* **9**, 201–6.

(83) GORDON, W. (1927). Der Compton Effekt nach der Schrödingerschen Theorie. *Z. Phys.* **40**, 117–33.

(84) GREGG, R.Q. and GINGRICH, N.S. (1940). *Rev. Sci. Instrum.* **11**, 305–7.

(85) VAN DER GRINTEN, W. (1932). Verwendung von monochromatischer Strahlung bei Röntgenstreuung an Gasen. *Phys. Z.* **33**, 769–70.

(86) VAN DER GRINTEN, W. (1933). Temperatureinfluss und Verwendung von monochromatischer Strahlung bei der Streuung von Röntgenstrahlen am Tetrachlorkohlenstoffgas. *Phys. Z.* **34**, 609–18.

(87)   VAN DER GRINTEN, W. and BRASSEUR, H. (1936). Use of a Geiger-Müller counter for the study of the diffraction of X-rays by a gas. *Nature, Lond.*, **137**, 657.

(88)   GUINIER, A. (1937). *C.R. Acad. Sci., Paris*, **204**, 1115–16.

*(89)   GÜNTHER, P. (1930). Die chemischen Wirkungen der Röntgenstrahlen. *Ergebn. tech. Röntgenk.* **1**, 61–8.

(90)   GÜNTHER, P. and LEICHTER, H. (1936). *Z. phys. Chem.* B, **34**, 443–60.

(91)   HARTREE, D.R. (1928). The wave mechanics of an atom with a non-Coulomb central field. *Proc. Camb. Phil. Soc.* **24**, 89–110, 111–32.

(92)   HARTREE, D.R. and HARTREE, W. (1936). Self-consistent field, with exchange, for Cl^-. *Proc. Roy. Soc.* A, **156**, 45–62.

(93)   HARVEY, G.G. (1934). The effect of pressure on the intensity of X-rays scattered from nitrogen at small angles. *Phys. Rev.* **46**, 441–5.

(94)   HEISENBERG, W. (1931). Über die inkohärente Streuung von Röntgenstrahlen. *Phys. Z.* **32**, 737–40.

(95)   HERZOG, G. (1929). Zerstreuung von Röntgenstrahlen an Gasen. I. *Helv. Phys. Acta*, **2**, 169–216.

(96)   HERZOG, G. (1929). Zerstreuung von Röntgenstrahlen an Gasen. II. *Helv. Phys. Acta*, **2**, 217–56.

(97)   HERZOG, G. (1931). Die Streuung von Röntgenstrahlen an Argon. *Z. Phys.* **69**, 207–34.

(98)   HERZOG, G. (1931). Die Streuung von Röntgenstrahlen an Neon und Argon. *Z. Phys.* **70**, 583–9.

(99)   HERZOG, G. (1931). Die Streuung von Röntgenstrahlen an Helium. *Z. Phys.* **70**, 590–4.

(100)   HERZOG, G. (1933). Absolutmessung der Streuintensität von Cu-$K\alpha$-Strahlung an Argon. *Helv. Phys. Acta*, **6**, 508–54.

(101)   HILL, J.A. and TERREY, H. (1937). *Phil. Mag.* **23**, 339–44.

(102)   HOFFMANN, K. (1938). Die Bestimmung der an Gasen incoherent gestreuten Röntgenstrahlung. *Phys. Z.* **39**, 695–706.

(103)   HÖNL, H. (1933). Atomfaktor für Röntgenstrahlen als Problem der Dispersionstheorie (*K*-Schale). *Ann. Phys., Lpz.*, **18**, 625–55.

(104)   HÖNL, H. (1933). Zur Dispersionstheorie der Röntgenstrahlen. *Z. Phys.* **84**, 1–16.

(105)   HUGHES, A.L. (1939). Scattering of fast electrons in gases. *Phys. Rev.* **55**, 350–2.

(106)   HUND, F. (1932). Berechnung der Elektronenverteilung in einer zweiatomigen Molekel nach der Methode von Thomas und Fermi. *Z. Phys.* **77**, 12–25.

(107)   JAMES, R.W., WALLER, J. and HARTREE, D.R. (1928). An investigation into the existence of zero-point energy in the rock-salt lattice by an X-ray diffraction method. *Proc. Roy. Soc.* A, **118**, 334–50.

(108)   JAMES, R.W., BRINDLEY, G.W. and WOOD, R.G. (1929). A quantitative study of the reflexion of X-rays from crystals of aluminium. *Proc. Roy. Soc.* A, **125**, 401–19.

(109) JAMES, R.W. and BRINDLEY, G.W. (1931). Some numerical calculations of atomic scattering factors. *Phil. Mag.* **12**, 81–112, 729.
JAMES, R.W. and BRINDLEY, G.W. (1931). Some numerical values of the atomic scattering factor. *Z. Kristallogr.* **78**, 470–76.

(110) JAMES, R.W. (1932). Über den Einfluss der Temperatur auf die Streuung der Röntgenstrahlen durch Gasmoleküle. *Phys. Z.* **33**, 737–54.

*(111) JAMES, R.W. (1933). Die absolute Bestimmung der Atomformfaktoren durch Versuche mit Kristallen. *Ergebn. techn. Röntgenk.* **3**, 32–45.

(112) JESSE, W.P. (1937). Experiments on the variation of the atomic structure factor of nickel with X-ray wave-length. *Phys. Rev.* **52**, 443–51.

(113) KAISER, R. (1935). Die Struktur der Sechsringe C_6H_6 und C_6Cl_6. *Phys. Z.* **36**, 92–9.

(114) KEESOM, W.H. and SMEDT, J. DE (1923). Sur la diffraction des rayons X par les liquides. *J. Phys. Radium*, [6], **4**, 144–51.

(115) KLEIN, O. and NISHINA, Y. (1929). Über die Streuung von Strahlung durch freie Elektronen nach der neuen relativistischen Quantendynamik von Dirac. *Z. Phys.* **52**, 853–68.

(116) KOLKMEIJER, N.H., KROM, C.J. and KUNST, H. (1937). *Nature, Lond.*, **140**, 67–8.

(117) KUNZL, V. (1935). *C.R. Acad. Sci., Paris*, **201**, 656–8.

(118) KUPER, J.B. (1938). The scattering of fast electrons in gases. *Phys. Rev.* **53**, 993–7.

*(119) LONSDALE, K. (1943). Experimental study of X-ray Scattering in relation to Crystal Dynamics. *Rep. Progr. Phys.* **9**, 256–93.

(120) LU, S.S. (1933). The scattering of X-rays by polyatomic gases. *Chinese J. Phys.* **1**, 51–73.

*(121) McMILLEN, J.H. (1939). Elastic electron scattering in gases. *Rev. Mod. Phys.* **11**, 84–110.

(122) MARK, H. and WIERL, R. (1930). Über Elektronenbeugung am einzelnen Molekül. *Naturwissenschaften*, **18**, 205.

(123) MARK, H. and WIERL, R. (1930). Atomformfaktorbestimmung mit Elektronen. *Z. Phys.* **60**, 741–53.

(124) MAXWELL, L.R., MOSLEY, V.M. and HENDRICKS, S.B. (1936). *Phys. Rev.* **50**, 41–5.

(125) MAXWELL, L.R., HENDRICKS, S.B. and MOSLEY, V.M. (1937). *Phys. Rev.* **52**, 968–72.

(126) MENKE, H. (1932). Röntgeninterferenzen an Flüssigkeiten (Hg, Ga, CCl_4). *Phys. Z.* **33**, 593–604.

(127) MEYER, H.H. (1930). *Ann. Phys., Lpz.*, **5**, 701–34.

(128) MORSE, P.M. (1932). Unelastische Streuung von Kathodenstrahlen. *Phys. Z.* **33**, 443–5.

(129) MOTT, N.F. (1930). The scattering of electrons by atoms. *Proc. Roy. Soc. A*, **127**, 658–65.

(130) MÜLLER, A. and CLAY, R.E. (1939). *J. Instn Elect. Engrs*, **84**, 261–8.

152   BIBLIOGRAPHY

(131) NIENS, W. (1936). Über Messung der Ergiebigkeit der Röntgen-
fluorescenz mittels des Zählrohres. *Ann. Phys., Lpz.*, **26**, 513–32.
(132) OHLIN, P. (1938). *Phys. Z.* **39**, 567–71.
(133) ORNSTEIN, L.S., BRINKMAN, H., HAUER, A. and TOL, T. (1938).
Photographic intensity-measurements of electron diffraction
patterns. *Physica*, **5**, 693–700.
(134) OTT, H. (1926). *Phys. Z.* **27**, 598–9.
(135) OWEN, E.A. (1911). *Proc. Camb. Phil. Soc.* **16**, 161–6.
(136) PAULING, L. and SHERMAN, J. (1932). Screening constants for
many-electron atoms. The calculation and interpretation of X-ray
term values, and the calculation of atomic scattering factors.
Z. Kristallogr. **81**, 1–29.
(137) PAULING, L. and BROCKWAY, L.O. (1935). The radial distribution
method of interpretation of electron diffraction photographs of
gas molecules. *J. Amer. Chem. Soc.* **57**, 2684–92.
(138) PIÉRARD, J. and VAN DER GRINTEN, W. (1935). Sur la diffraction
des rayons X par le CCl_4 gazeux et sa structure géométrique.
IIe Congrès National des Sciences, pp. 346–8. Bruxelles.
(139) PIÉRARD, J. (1936). Sur la diffraction des X rayons par le $CHCl_3$
gazeux. *Bull. Soc. Roy. Sci. Liège*, pp. 205–6.
(140) PIÉRARD, J. (1936). Sur la diffraction des rayons X par le CCl_4
gazeux. *Mèm. Soc. Roy. Sci. Liège* [4], **1**, 441–70.
(141) PIERCE, W.C. (1933). The scattering of X-rays by the gaseous
dichlorbenzenes. *Phys. Rev.* **43**, 145–6.
(142) PIERCE, W.C. (1934). X-ray diffraction by gaseous benzene deri-
vatives. *J. Chem. Phys.* **2**, 1–5.
(143) PIRENNE, M.H. (1938). Diffraction des rayons X par le silicochloro-
forme gazeux. Structure géométrique de la molécule $SiCHl_3$.
C.R. Acad. Sci., Paris, **206**, 516–17.
(144) PIRENNE, M.H. (1939). Untersuchung des Moleküls $SiHCl_3$ mit
Röntgeninterferenzen. *Phys. Z.* **40**, 145–58.
*(145) PIRENNE, M.H. (1939). The diffraction of X-rays by gas molecules.
A comparison with electron diffraction and a discussion of the
results for $SiHCl_3$. *J. Chem. Phys.* **7**, 144–55.
(146) PRINS, J.A. (1929). Über die Beugung von Röntgenstrahlen in
Flüssigkeiten und Lösungen. *Z. Phys.* **56**, 617–48.
(147) RAMAN, SIR C.V. (1928). A classical derivation of the Compton
effect. *Indian J. Phys.* **3**, 357–69.
(148) RAMSAUER, R. (1937). Über die Streuung von Röntgenstrahlen
an gasförmigen Alkoholen und die Grenzen der Anwendbarkeit
des Verfahrens bei leichten Molekülen. *Z. phys. Chem. B*, **35**,
139–63.
*(149) RANDALL, J.T. (1934). *The Diffraction of X-rays and Electrons by
Amorphous Solids, Liquids and Gases*. London.
(150) RENNINGER, M. (1937). Röntgenographische Beiträge zur Kenntnis
der Ladungsverteilung im Diamantgitter. *Z. Kristallogr.* **97**, 107–21.
(151) RICHTER, H. (1932). Streuung von Röntgenstrahlen am Chlor.
Phys. Z. **33**, 587–8.

(152) RICHTER, H. (1935). Interferometrische Messungen mit Röntgen-strahlen am Chlor, Methan und Trimethylamin. *Phys. Z.* **36**, 85–91.

(153) ROSS, P.A. (1928). *J. Opt. Soc. Amer.* **16**, 433–7.

(154) SCHERRER, P. and STÄGER, A. (1928). Zerstreuung von Röntgen-strahlen an Quecksilberdampf. *Helv. Phys. Acta*, **1**, 518–33.

(155) SCHOPPE, R. (1936). Streuung von Röntgenstrahlen an Halogen-benzolen. *Z. phys. Chem.* B, **34**, 461–70.

(156) SHERMAN, J. (1933). A four-place table of sin x/x. *Z. Kristallogr.* **85**, 404–19.

(157) STEWART, G.W. and MORROW, R.M. (1927). *Phys. Rev.* **30**, 232–44.

*(158) STUART, H.A. (1934). *Molekülstruktur.* Berlin.

(159) STUART, H.A. (1937). Valenzwinkel und Wirkungsradius gebun-dener Atome. *Z. phys. Chem.* B, **36**, 155–62.

(160) THIBAUD, J. and TRILLAT, J.J. (1930). *Z. Phys.* **61**, 816–36.

(161) THOMAS, L.H. (1926). The calculation of atomic fields. *Proc. Camb. Phil. Soc.* **23**, 542–8.

(162) THOMER, G. (1937). Streuung von Röntgenstrahlen an neonähn-lichen Molekülen und an C_6H_6. *Phys. Z.* **38**, 48–57.

*(163) THOMSON, SIR J.J. *Conduction of Electricity through Gases*, 1st ed., Cambridge, 1903; 2nd ed. 1906; 3rd ed. with G.P. THOMSON, Vol. I, 1928, Vol. II, 1933.

*(164) TRIESCHMANN, H.G. (1936). Kohärente Streuung von Röntgen-strahlen an Atomen und Molekülen. In Eucken-Wolf, *Hand- und Jahrbuch der Chemischen Physik*, **8**, II, B.

(165) TURKEVITCH, A. and BEACH, J.Y. (1939). *J. Amer. Chem. Soc.* **61**, 3127–30.

(166) VALLARTA, M.S. and ROSEN, N. (1932). The relativistic Thomas-Fermi atom. *Phys. Rev.* **41**, 708–12.

(167) WAGNER, E. and KULENKAMPFF, H. (1922). *Ann. Phys., Lpz.*, **68**, 369–413.

(168) WALLER, I. (1923). Zur Frage der Einwirkung der Wärmebewegung auf die Interferenz von Röntgenstrahlen. *Z. Phys.* **17**, 398–408.

(169) WALLER, I. and JAMES, R.W. (1927). On the temperature factors of X-ray reflexion for sodium and chlorine in the rock-salt crystal. *Proc. Roy. Soc.* A, **117**, 214–23.

(170) WALLER, I. (1927). On the scattering of radiation from atoms. *Phil. Mag.* **4**, 1228–37.

(171) WALLER, I. (1928). Über eine verallgemeinerte Streuungsformel. *Z. Phys.* **51**, 213–31.

(172) WALLER, I. and HARTREE, D.R. (1929). On the intensity of total scattering of X-rays. *Proc. Roy. Soc.* A, **124**, 119–42.

(173) WENTZEL, G. (1927). Zur Theorie des Comptoneffekts. I. *Z. Phys.* **43**, 1–8.

(174) WENTZEL, G. (1927). Zur Theorie des Comptoneffekts. II. *Z. Phys.* **43**, 779–87.

(175) WOLLAN, E.O. (1931). Note on scattering by diatomic gases. *Proc. Nat. Acad. Sci., Wash.*, **17**, 475–9.

(176) WOLLAN, E.O. (1931). Scattering of X-rays from gases. *Phys. Rev.* **37**, 862–72.

(177) WOLLAN, E.O. (1931). Experimental electron distributions in atoms of monatomic gases. *Phys. Rev.* **38**, 15–22.

*(178) WOLLAN, E.O. (1932). X-ray scattering and atomic structure. *Rev. Mod. Phys.* **4**, 205–58.

(179) WOLLAN, E.O. (1933). Measurements of intensity of Compton modified radiation by means of filters. *Phys. Rev.* **43**, 955–63.

(180) WOO, Y.H. (1930). On the intensity of total scattering of X-rays by monatomic gases. *Proc. Nat. Acad. Sci., Wash.*, **16**, 814–16.

(181) YEARIAN, H.J. (1941). *Phys. Rev.* **59**, 926.

(182) ZERNIKE, F. and PRINS, J.A. (1927). Die Beugung von Röntgenstrahlen in Flüssigkeiten als Effekt der Molekülanordnung. *Z. Phys.* **41**, 184–94.

(183) FINBAK, C. (1937). *Avh. norske VidenskAkad.* M.-N. Kl. 1937, no. 13.

(184) FINBAK, C., HASSEL, O. and OTTAR, B. (1941). Application of the rotating sector method to the electron diffraction determination of gaseous CCl_4 and CBr_4. *Arch. Math. Naturv.* B, **44**, no. 13.

(185) FINBAK, C. (1941). Electron diffraction by gases. Determination of radial distribution functions from sector-diagrams. *Avh. norske VidenskAkad.* M.-N. Kl. 1941, no. 7.

(186) *Internationale Tabellen zur Bestimmung von Kristallstrukturen* (1935), 2 vols. Berlin.

*(187) MAXWELL, L. R. (1940). The electronic diffraction method. *J. Opt. Soc. Amer.* **30**, 374–95.

SUBJECT INDEX

AUTHOR INDEX

4-7-47 · Bookstore